Tales from the Madhouse
An insider critique of psychiatric services

by Gary L. Sidley

PCCS Books
Monmouth

First published 2015

PCCS Books Ltd.
Wyastone Business Park
Wyastone Leys
Monmouth
NP25 3SR
UK
Tel +44 (0)1600 891 509
www.pccs-books.co.uk

The author has asserted his right to be identified as the author of this work in accordance with the Copyright, Designs and Patents Act 1988.

Tales from the Madhouse: An insider critique of psychiatric services

A CIP catalogue record for this book is available from the British Library

ISBN 978 1 906254 75 9

Cover designed in the UK by Old Dog Graphics
Typeset in the UK by Raven Books
Printed in the UK by Imprint Digital, Exeter

Dedication

This book is dedicated to my wife Sue,
my son Ryan, and my daughter Rebecca

contents

foreword

There have been many recent advances in the delivery and organisation of mental health services, including an increased emphasis on the involvement of service users in both service design and delivery, increasing access to a range of evidence-based interventions and the promotion of recovery as an outcome. There are some examples of service models that have embraced these principles and philosophies, such as many of the early intervention services for young people with psychosis that were established over the last decade in the UK. The best examples of such services provide a framework for collaboration between service users, families and mental health professionals to work together to achieve the goals that are identified by the service user. Within this context the professionals embrace both users and carers as partners in the delivery of services and offer their expert knowledge to help service users make informed choices about which interventions may be most useful and acceptable to them. They can then use their expert skills to provide these interventions in a way that is consistent with best practice, as outlined in clinical guidelines such as those developed by NICE.

Gary Sidley has some experience of working within and leading such services, and I have had the pleasure of a long working relationship with Gary in which I have witnessed his significant contributions to the development of such environments. However, he has also had a long career in which he has spent many years working in less progressive clinical environments, from long-stay institutions to acute psychiatric wards and community-based mental health services. It is clear from reading this book that Gary is rightly frustrated by the failures of mental health providers to deliver high-quality and acceptable services on a routine basis.

His warmth and empathy for the difficulties faced by service users stands in stark contrast to some of the examples of 'service' provision that he describes. (This reminds me of the objection to the term 'service user' by a colleague of mine – Yvonne – who has lived experience of psychosis;

she points out that to call what she has received a 'service' is both insulting and in breach of the Trade Descriptions Act.) Gary highlights the gap between evidence and practice, and between guidelines and implementation, using a combination of accessible reviews of research evidence on important topics and illustrative anecdotes that demonstrate the sad consequences of instances when this gap is not bridged (and in some cases is exacerbated by services). Another service user colleague of mine, Martina, likened the recovery journeys travelled by people with psychosis to a game of snakes and ladders; she suggested that the involvement of services is often experienced as a snake that can hinder recovery rather than a ladder that can facilitate it.

Many of the illustrations from Gary's experience also demonstrate this. The themes that are identified are not rocket science – the importance of collaboration and respect in order to avoid a them-and-us culture between staff and service users that serves to maintain stigma and discrimination, and the importance of accountability and action when staff values, attitudes and behaviour are found wanting. Similarly, the importance of an individualised approach based on a broad understanding of the person (such as is offered by psychological formulation) is central to the delivery of effective and acceptable mental health services. The providers and commissioners of mental health services should be able to address such challenges in a systematic way. However, Gary also highlights some of the barriers to such progress, many of which are about maintenance of the status quo: services designed for the benefit of staff rather than service users; a service model for mental health based on the traditional (but unfounded) medical assumption that what we require most to treat illness is hospital beds, doctors and nurses; and large power imbalances between professionals and service users as well as between professions. In the words of a past president of the American Psychiatric Association: 'We must examine the fact that as a profession, we have allowed the biopsychosocial model to become the bio-bio-bio model' (Sharfstein, 2005, p. 3). Developing a truly bio-psychosocial model, in which each approach has equivalent status, respect and investment, and where service users are at the centre of decision making, is likely to facilitate the transformation of mental health services into a configuration that is fit for purpose.

Gary outlines some possibilities for a way forward, and it is to be hoped that we can learn lessons from past abuses and inadequacies that can change things for the better. Gary writes with a tone that is demanding rather than conciliatory. Given that his admirable attempts at conciliation and diplomacy when working on the inside within services did not create the changes he was striving for, a more assertive approach now he is on the outside of services is understandable. Hopefully, this book will enable potential service users and carers (which is every one of us), as well as commissioners and providers, to use evidence to know what to ask for from services. Similarly, an awareness of the examples of poor individual practice and structural inadequacies that are outlined in this book can be used to inform how such services should be delivered (and how they should not).

Tony Morrison, July 2014

reference

Sharfstein, S.S. (2005). Big Pharma and American psychiatry: The good, the bad, and the ugly. *Psychiatric News*, August 19, 3.

preface

Psychiatry is a fundamentally flawed discipline routinely delivering a form of institutionalised discrimination that detrimentally impacts on the lives of many people already blighted by distress and misery. The engine room for its deleterious practices is psychiatry's stubborn, fallacious and self-serving insistence that the range of human suffering construed as 'mental illness' primarily represents the manifestation of some form of biological aberration. The pervasiveness of this government-sponsored malpractice across the Western world, maintained by the powerful vested interests of professional psychiatry and the pharmaceutical industry, amounts to a modern-day scandal.

My striking indictment of the current state of psychiatry represents a considered view, shaped by 33 years of continuous employment in the UK's mental health services. I first embarked on a career in psychiatry in 1980 when, as a naïve 21-year-old, I successfully applied for a post as an unqualified nursing assistant on an acute inpatient unit, trying to help people identified as suffering with mental illnesses such as 'schizophrenia', 'manic depression' (later to be referred to as 'bipolar disorder'), and 'endogenous depression' (a severe form of melancholy purported to have arisen in the absence of aversive environmental factors). Over the subsequent three decades I performed a variety of professional roles including student psychiatric nurse, psychiatric staff nurse, psychiatric charge nurse, senior nurse; team manager, clinical psychologist, and professional lead for psychology. During this time I have worked in a traditional psychiatric asylum, district general hospitals, and countless community mental health centres and GP practices.

In delivering a damning critique of a system in which I have worked throughout my adult life, I do not wish to imply that I am a saintly figure who has consistently remained aloof to the murky activities of the psychiatric world. I too am culpable. During the early years of my career, I chaperoned patients to their electroconvulsive therapy (ECT) treatments and actively participated in the process of inflicting an electric shock to their brains, the voltage reaching a magnitude that would necessitate an urgent visit to the accident and emergency department of the local hospital if it had occurred in any other setting. My history is further tainted by my involvement in the forcible drugging of patients in the early 1980s while working within the old psychiatric asylum.

Even after the completion of my clinical psychology training in 1989, and my growing realisation that there are more helpful and enabling ways of making sense of human suffering than assuming it to be the product of disturbed brain biochemistry, I habitually colluded with aspects of the dominant medical paradigm, typically rationalising my conformity as a strategic manoeuvre to preserve positive relationships with managers and other clinicians and thereby retain influence to counter the excesses of biological psychiatry. A respected senior psychology colleague would often urge me to show patience and aim for modest, incremental improvements within the existing system; to strive for 'evolution not revolution'. His counsel showed recognition of the fact that there were many conscientious and compassionate colleagues, from all professional disciplines, delivering piecemeal examples of therapeutic practice, and my energies might best be channelled towards collaborating with, and further developing, these positive initiatives.

However, by the turn of the century my disillusionment with our biologically skewed psychiatric service had intensified. For the final decade or so of my career in the National Health Service I laboured under mounting recognition that effective and enabling responses to human suffering could not be attained (at least not in an enduring way) solely by incremental, evolutionary changes to the existing system. A paradigm shift (something approximating to a revolution) would be necessary if, as a society, we were to meaningfully promote or restore positive mental health within our fellow citizens.

At the time of writing I believe that such a shift in the way that Western societies make sense of mental health problems is imminent. An unprecedented collective of stakeholders are currently highlighting the fundamental flaws within our psychiatric system and are clamouring for change. The dissenters include academics, journalists, a plethora of patients with first-hand experience of using mental health services, and a range of professionals that includes an increasingly vocal band of psychiatrists. Despite the formidable power base of the medical profession (of which psychiatry claims to represent a legitimate branch) it is my hope and expectation that a combination of economic pressures and shifting attitudes will trigger a radical revision of the way our society addresses human suffering.

The writing of this book has been a cathartic experience, providing me with a vehicle to express my cumulative frustration consequent to many years of working in a fundamentally flawed and pernicious psychiatric arena. Witnessing how the worthy efforts of many individuals within the psychiatric system to promote more humane and empowering responses to people in distress are frustrated by the dominant medical paradigm has been exasperating; the opportunity to express the nonsense, injustices and punitive responses delivered, on a daily basis, under the banner of professional psychiatry has been liberating. Yet my main motive for writing this book is not personal remediation, but the hope that I can contribute, albeit in a modest way, to the groundswell of dissent striving to realise radical change to the way we make sense of human distress.

The book presents an insider perspective on all that is wrong with Western psychiatry. Each chapter (apart from the last) is divided into two sections. The first comprises a concise but scholarly review of a topic pertinent to mental health services in the developed world – for example, stigma, power imbalances and the toxic collaboration between biological psychiatry and the pharmaceutical industry. The second part of each chapter offers detailed anecdotal observations, all based on personal experience, that vividly illustrate how the topic in question plays out within the psychiatric arena. I hope this mix of academic evaluation and informal storytelling will interest a wide range of people, including mental health professionals, service users and general readers concerned by the way our society responds to human suffering.

I expect a polarised response to my expressed views; any commentary on the state of contemporary psychiatry inevitably evokes passionate reactions. I welcome considered criticism of my assertions regarding the perniciousness of contemporary psychiatry and my proposals for how we might realise more enabling responses to people in distress. Informed debate can be constructive, enabling us to reach a shared understanding of the specific issue under scrutiny. Conversely, attempts to simplistically dismiss my viewpoint as the product of 'turf wars' between psychiatry and psychology, or as the vindictive ramblings of a disaffected ex-employee, betray laziness on the part of the responder and an unwillingness to reflect on the specific criticisms raised. Nor do I lack compassion for people enduring misery and anguish; I am confident that the vast majority of service users and professional staff I have worked alongside throughout my career would confirm I am a caring individual who strives to improve the lives of those afflicted. Nor am I a scientologist, a label some of my American associates have applied to me after reading my criticisms of the dominant medical paradigm.

The way I see it is that I am a clinician who, while working alongside numerous people suffering anguish and misery, increasingly realised that the psychiatric system within which I operated was based on pseudo-scientific assumptions that were barely more valid than those of witchcraft and demonic possession which dominated society's approach to madness in bygone centuries. I still find it astonishing that modern Western societies, endowed with an abundance of scientific expertise and ever mindful of prejudicial practices, continues to collude with an institution – professional psychiatry – that is fallacious and discriminatory in equal measure.

I apologise to readers for the frequent use of medical terminology within this book. Language is important, and routine use of terms such as 'psychosis', 'depression', 'symptoms' and 'treatment' can perpetuate the misleading notion that human distress is the product of a biological illness of the brain in much the same way as cancer is an illness of the body. Regrettably, the medical model approach to mental health problems is so deeply entrenched in the psyche of professional and layperson alike that such terms cannot be avoided without my writing becoming incomprehensible. The legislation referred to in the book refers primarily to the legal framework in England and Wales; although different in the detail, the mental health laws in the USA and other Western countries tend to adhere to similar principles.

Finally, although all the anecdotes contained within the book refer to real events, the names, places and some circumstantial details have been changed so as to protect identities. Nevertheless, given that many of the events described are not uncommon, a number of service users might suspect that an anecdote refers to their own experiences.

acknowledgements

I owe a debt of gratitude to a multitude of people who, at various points during the last 33 years, provided me with guidance, learning opportunities, support and a safe forum in which to discuss the issues addressed in this book. In particular I would like to thank my work colleagues, both those from the clinical psychology arena (including Catherine Allen, Fairuz Awenat, Alan Barrett, Sian Bensa, Richard Bentall, Samantha Bowe, Aiden Bucknall, Laura Golding, Kate Hellin, Stephanie Kennedy, Ian Lowens, Jill McGarry, Helen Morey, Sandra Neil, Zoe Rivers, Richard Shillitoe, Mary Shinner, Angela Smith, Stephanie Sneider, Sara Tai, Alan Tatham and Mary Welford) and those from other disciplines (including Lynn Agnew, Mike Buckley, Clive Bullock, Rachel Clarke, Sarah Cleverly, Kevin Corran, Steve Crossley, David Entwistle, Heather Femia, Paul French, Rebecca Glentworth, Teresa Grogan, Jeanette Houghton, Nofie Johnston, Jim Leech, Tara McGinley, Debbie Sharples and Claire Watson).

I am eternally grateful to all the service users who allowed me privileged access to their personal stories at a time in their lives when they were at their most vulnerable. Collectively, you taught me a huge amount about the nature of human suffering, the traumatic experiences that are central to its genesis, and the courage and resilience required to achieve the peace associated with self-acceptance.

A special thanks to Yvonne Awenat, Wendy Broderick and Colin Mattinson, my training collaborators at the Greater Manchester West Health and Wellbeing Academy; their lived experiences of mental health problems, along with their skills and enthusiasm, have injected a wonderful authenticity into our teaching sessions.

Also I would like to express my appreciation to Melissa Pyle for sharing her expertise about stigma, and to Tony Morrison for his generosity in taking time out from the huge demands of academia to write the Foreword (and, perhaps most importantly, for continuing to be a thoroughly decent human being, despite his world renown in the research arena).

Finally, Heather Allan and Sandy Green at PCCS Books deserve recognition for their encouragement, support, guidance and unwavering patience shown throughout the publication process.

1

the psychiatric asylum

part I: the doctors assume control of the mentally disordered

At the peak of their popularity in the 1950s, psychiatric institutions (or asylums) hosted around 150,000 citizens of the United Kingdom who were adjudged to be incapable of community living. The comparable figure in the USA was estimated to be half a million (Porter, 2002). The historical events that led to this mass human warehousing involved the actions of legislators and physicians, typically executed with laudable intentions. Part I of this chapter will outline these contributions to the emergence of the large psychiatric asylums, while highlighting some of the embryonic shoots of our flawed modern-day psychiatric system. The second section will share anecdotes to illustrate what life was like within these unique institutions.

before the state-run asylum

Prior to the proliferation of the state-run psychiatric asylums, the responsibility of supervising the insane typically defaulted to the family. Ignorance about the basis of madness, including lingering associations with demonic possession, often evoked shame when a family member became afflicted. Victims of what today would be called stigma, families kept their lunatic relative hidden indoors, often under the supervision of servants in the cellar or farm hands in the outhouses.

Throughout the middle ages, outside of the home the foremost support for the insane was provided by religious organisations. Most famously, the shrine of St Dymphna in the Belgium village of Gheel became a magnet for the mentally defective, many transported there by family members hoping for a miraculous cure for their loved ones. In fifteenth-century Spain, asylums emerged under religious auspices at Seville, Valencia and many other cities, providing a compassionate brand of psychiatric care. Parallel developments in the United Kingdom focused on the Bethlem

Royal Hospital in London. Founded in 1207 as a religious house (St Mary of Bethlem), the hospital evolved into one of the oldest lunatic asylums, admitting its first mentally disordered patient in 1407.

As affluence grew in the late eighteenth and early nineteenth centuries, families were more willing to pay for outside help to look after their disturbed relatives. To meet this swelling demand, private madhouses proliferated. The quality of care provided by these 'run for profit' establishments varied widely, their inner workings often remaining hidden from scrutiny, families (shamed by the prospect of others knowing about their relatives' mental disorders) colluding with the madhouse owners to avert publicity.

State interference in restricting the freedoms of those deemed insane, under the guise of protecting society, has often exercised anti-psychiatry commentators, most famously Szasz, who viewed 'institutional psychiatry' as a means of protecting society rather than benefiting the individual (Szasz, 1973). An early example of state intervention that led to those deemed mentally defective being confined in general hospitals across Europe occurred in the seventeenth century. Petty criminals, prostitutes, beggars and the insane were removed from the streets. Such practice was particularly common in France; by 1660 Paris's Hôpital Général housed 6,000 such 'undesirables'.

moral treatment

In response to the inhumane conditions prevalent within many private asylums, a compassionate brand of psychiatric care evolved in the late eighteenth century that, for several decades, provided a counterbalance to the scalpels and leeches of the physicians. In the United Kingdom, the pioneer for this moral treatment was William Tuke, who founded the York Retreat in 1796.

Originating from a Quaker family, Tuke was a social activist who had earlier campaigned for the abolition of slavery. After witnessing the conditions in a York asylum where a close friend had died, Tuke's philanthropic energies were reassigned to the welfare of the mentally ill. Within the York Retreat, power imbalances between staff and patients were minimised. Residents were treated humanely, while self-control and self-discipline were encouraged through a consistent application of praise and punishment. Moreover, this moral treatment achieved excellent results and emerged as one of the most influential approaches to the treatment of mentally disordered people in asylums throughout Europe in the early nineteenth century.

Despite Tuke's son and grandson directing the York Retreat after his death, and publicising Tuke's methods in books, prophetically it was a medical practitioner who gained most credit for this innovative form of treatment. Philippe Pinel, considered by some to be the 'founder of modern psychiatry' (Shorter, 1997), had intended to develop his career in medicine when he moved to Paris in 1778, but was initially prohibited from doing so because his degree had been achieved in the provinces. Despite the lack of support from the medical establishment, Pinel continued to work as a journalist and unlicensed asylum physician. It was only when the medical profession's old guard lost influence during the French Revolution that Pinel gained access to the important position of Physician-in-Chief to the public asylums in Paris, allowing him to promote a more humane form of intervention for the mentally disordered.

Pinel's compassionate brand of psychiatric practice had been shaped by the work of Tuke in England. Furthermore, an appreciable amount of the reform of the Parisian asylums was undertaken by Pinel's assistant, an ex-patient called Jean-Baptiste Pussin (Schuster, Hoertel & Limosin, 2011). Despite the considerable contributions of non-medical pioneers, Tuke and Pussin, to the development of moral treatment, it was Pinel the physician who was touted as the man who freed the mad from their chains, thereby strengthening the claim that medical men, not laymen, were the experts in treating insanity.

Sadly, between the early eighteenth century and the present, this compassionate seam of psychiatric treatment lost its way among the reductionist fog that spawned interventions involving insulin-induced comas, leucotomies and electrocution.

state and medicine align

In the late eighteenth century, legislation emerged that began the enduring alliance between the state and the medical profession by formalising the role of physicians in the management of the insane. The Madhouse Act (1774) dictated that all private asylums had to be licensed and submit to an annual inspection. Doctors commonly played the role of overseers; the inspecting body in London was provided by the Royal College of Physicians. Furthermore, once licensing was established, to legitimise someone's confinement in an asylum all inmates (with the exception of paupers) required a letter from a medical practitioner.

Additional legislation in the early nineteenth century consolidated the medical profession's position as marshals of the mentally disordered. Various laws introduced in the 1820s necessitated the presence of a resident physician within both public and private asylums. The Lunacy Act (1845) required the establishment of Commissioners in Lunacy, a permanent body of asylum inspectors whose salaried members were a combination of lawyers and doctors. Medical supervision of psychiatric institutions was, however, no guarantee of service quality, a notorious example being the Bethlem Royal Hospital in London (mentioned above) which witnessed a series of corrupt practices during the tenure of four generations of the Monro family (all physicians) between 1728 and 1855 (Andrews et al., 1997).

physicians expand their influence

Although often invited into the asylums during the era of moral treatment, for their authority as much as their medical expertise, physicians soon imposed their distinctive brand of control and categorisation. William Battie became physician at London's St Luke's Asylum in the mid-eighteenth century and installed a more enlightened form of treatment than the cruelty, emetics and blood-letting of his Monro adversaries at the Bethlem. Nevertheless, his distinction between 'original insanity' (incurable) and 'consequential insanity' (resulting from a person's life experiences and curable) was a forerunner to various permutations of the endogenous-versus-reactive distinction which in the present day, as applied to psychosis and depression, continues to be spurious and unhelpful.

In addition to categorising the mentally disordered, as the nineteenth century progressed, further amendments to the Lunacy Act reinforced the position of the medical men as gatekeepers to the asylums. By the 1890s two medical certificates were required for the detention of all patients. One important consequence of this change was that, once detained in an asylum, it was typically a long time before the patient was considered for release.

Parallel developments occurred in the USA. A collective of 13 physicians specialising in mental disorders banded together in 1844 to form the Association of Medical Superintendents of American Institutions for the Insane (later to mutate into the formidable American Psychiatric Association).

expanding the asylums

Throughout the nineteenth century the number of asylum inmates increased exponentially. Legislation, in the form of the County Asylum Act (1808) and County Asylum/Lunacy Act (1845), required counties to fund the building of institutions to house their lunatics and to levy a rate for this purpose.

Initially, this expansion was fuelled by optimism and worthy aims. The growing popularity of moral treatments – viewing the mentally disordered as patients deserving of care rather than as prisoners deserving of punishment – led to a widespread expectation that the majority of those afflicted could be helped if given access to a more humanitarian approach. Furthermore, the authorities hoped that building the new asylums close to the existing workhouses would allow the many pauper lunatics languishing therein at the start of the nineteenth century to be rehoused in a more therapeutic setting.

Unfortunately, as the nineteenth century progressed, optimism waned. The ambitious claims by physicians that they could cure any disorder led to the asylums becoming silted up with patients suffering neurological deficits (those associated with syphilis, epilepsy and dementia). Consequently, cure rates declined and asylums became grossly overcrowded, a typical example being the Prestwich Asylum near Manchester that opened in 1851 to accommodate 350 patients; by 1900 it housed over 3,000. Along with this growing pessimism, the medically dominated asylums switched their emphasis from a curative role to that of custodian, confining the inmates to prevent them from breeding more of their kind.

While the increasingly chronic nature of the inmates' mental disorders was one factor responsible for swelling the asylum population, another was the often-dubious reason for committing someone to the psychiatric institution. From the late nineteenth century to the mid-twentieth century, women who bore illegitimate children or who found themselves trapped in unhappy marriages were at risk of being certified to the asylum (Porter, 2002). The criteria for legitimately concluding that someone is suffering from a mental disorder of sufficient severity to justify involuntary incarceration have always been contentious, and the medical practitioners gate-keeping entry to the asylums have often been swayed in their judgements by the prevalent culture and whim of the time. One stark example of the arbitrary diagnosis of madness is with regards to women who were compulsorily detained in a psychiatric asylum purely in response to requests from their husbands. Thus, in 1851 the state of Illinois in the USA enacted a statute that 'married women … may be received and detained at the hospital on the request of the husband of the woman … without the evidence of insanity or distraction required in other cases' (Szasz, 2006). So if a wife was deemed a nuisance by her spouse she could, on his say-so alone, be shipped to the local mental institution.

It is informative to inspect the detailed medical records of some of the people admitted to the large asylums. The rationales (presumably proffered by the medical attendants) for admission to the Willard State Hospital in New York (Penney, Stastny & Rinzler, 2008) included a reference to one alcohol-infused male who was 'singing and shouting and whistling in a boisterous manner'. Another future patient, a female, was described as 'excited, noisy ... silly and childish'. In England in 1900, the Prestwich Asylum removed a 25-year-old woman from the Manchester streets for exhibiting problems of 'drink and immorality' (Greater Manchester Council Record Office, 2008).

life in the asylum

Although asylums, particularly in the early stages of their existence, diverged in the quality of care on offer (ranging from chaining and punishment to compassion and support), a number of fundamental commonalities emerged. Perhaps the most striking feature of life within the psychiatric institution was rigid routine. Order was paramount, and daily life for the inmates was regimented. Meals, sleep, work and leisure were allocated to fixed time slots within each day.

The emphasis on regimentation meant that individuality was sacrificed. A typical ward in an asylum housed up to 50 patients, thereby compromising privacy and human dignity. Individual preferences were discouraged or ignored.

A further striking characteristic of asylum life was self-containment. Although in later years the inmates were encouraged to leave the grounds and visit their local towns, for the most part the large asylums incorporated their own shops, cafés, farms and industrial units whose products would be sold to raise money for in-house social events. Local craftsmen were employed by the asylums to teach the patients new skills. In keeping with the gender expectations of the time, men engaged in joinery or work on the farm while women found employment in the sewing rooms or kitchens. Occasionally, the more diligent workers could create a specialist role for themselves within the institution; for example, for several decades 'Laurence' from the Willard State Hospital operated as the grave-digger, as well as preparing the corpses for burial – functions he apparently carried out with aplomb (Penney et al., 2008).

As the asylum population swelled and therapeutic optimism declined, security was emphasised, while the sedating of inmates to aid compliance became more popular as the twentieth century progressed. Also, the pool of patients within the psychiatric institutions was increasingly differentiated into categories: incurables from the curables, the clean from the dirty, and the improving from the long-stay.

In summary, although a brief overview of the rise and decline of the mental asylum rightly incorporates well-intentioned practices intended to improve the lives of the mentally disordered – moral treatments, for example – the seedlings of the fundamental flaws of modern psychiatric services can be detected within the activities of these Victorian institutions. The symbiotic relationship between the state and the medical profession; the simplistic and often-fallacious categorisation of the mentally disordered; the loss of human individuality and the de-emphasising of personal meaning; and the arbitrary 'diagnosis' of mental illnesses and the valuing of compliance – characteristics that remain rife within current psychiatric provision – can all be recognised within the workings of the old mental asylums.

references

Andrews, J., Briggs, A., Porter, R., Tucker, P. & Waddington, K. (1997). *The History of Bethlem*. London & New York: Routledge.

Greater Manchester Council Record Office. (2008). *Safety in Numbers: Life inside Prestwich Asylum in 1900.*

Penney, D., Stastny, P. & Rinzler, L. (2008). *The Lives They Left Behind: Suitcases from a state hospital attic*. New York: Bellevue Literary Press.

Porter, R. (2002). *Madness: A brief history*. Oxford: Oxford University Press.

Schuster, J.P., Hoertel, N. & Limosin, F. (2011). The man behind Philippe Pinel: Jean-Baptiste Pussin (1746–1811) – psychiatry in pictures. *British Journal of Psychiatry, 198*, 241.

Shorter, E. (1997). *A History of Psychiatry: From the era of the asylum to the age of Prozac*. New York: John Wiley & Sons.

Szasz, T.S. (1973). *The Manufacture of Madness: A comparative study of the Inquisition and the mental health movement*. London: Routledge & Keegan Paul.

Szasz, T.S. (2006). Psychiatry: A branch of the law. *The Freeman, 56*, 18–20 (December). Retrieved 21 April 2014 from http://www.szasz.com/freeman17.html

part II: routine and conformity

task allocation

My alarm clock screeched and I fumbled for the button to end the din. Squinting from my bed I became aware of the time, 6.00 am. A wave of apprehension, mixed with bursts of excitement, rippled upwards from my abdomen as my befuddled brain registered the beginning of my first day of work on the wards of a large psychiatric institution, known locally as the Prestwich Asylum.

It was mid-October 1981. Six weeks earlier I had begun my psychiatric-nurse training (a three-year course to qualify as a Registered Mental Nurse) but had spent the whole of this time in a classroom receiving instruction about how to read a medication prescription card and other essential tasks, as well as practising my injection technique on oranges (as a prelude to being let loose on human buttocks). But today was the first day of my placement on Fullwood Ward where I would be allowed direct access to the mentally disordered inmates.

Clad in my new grey suit with matching waistcoat, the standard hospital uniform for male nurses, I walked the short distance from the nurses' residence to the ward and crossed the threshold into the surreal world of the mental asylum.

Despite the early hour, 7 o'clock in the morning, several of the residents were already wandering around the day room, many of them shouting or crying. Not knowing what to do, and mindful of not appearing intimidated in the eyes of the other nursing staff, I ambled to the dormitory doors and peered in at the two long rows of beds. The stench of faeces and urine was eye-watering. As I tried to stifle my growing nausea, I felt a hand on my shoulder causing me to spin.

'Have you seen Glenda? I can't find my shirt for work and I'm going to miss my bus if I don't get a move on.' An old man, probably in his early 80s, wearing only a pyjama top and naked from the waist down, was looking directly into my eyes.

'I'm sorry, I've only just started on the ward today,' I mumbled. 'I don't know who Glenda is.'

'Glenda, my wife Glenda,' replied the old man, frustration evident in his tone of voice.

At this point a female nursing assistant intervened, linked arms with the patient and led him away, saying, 'Come on Ted, let's leave this young man in peace and go and find some clothes for you to put on.'

Fullwood Ward was classified as a 'psycho-geriatric' ward housing 38 mainly elderly gentlemen afflicted with a variety of senile dementias but also some younger males with profound movement disorders such as Huntington's chorea (a genetic disorder causing cognitive impairment, involuntary writhing movements, and mood instability). The dementia sufferers who were mobile typically spent their days wandering confused and disorientated around the ward. Others with coexisting physical impairments spent the daylight hours sitting in chairs in the day room, some strapped in for their own safety.

On the morning of my first day, the senior nurse-in-charge (a man with over 20 years of experience working in the institution) provided me, and the other student nurses, with an introduction to the ward.

'Routine and order are essential', he said, 'or key tasks will be overlooked and the unit will descend into chaos.'

All nursing jobs had to be allocated a set time, and he pointed to a weekly planner on the wall of the nursing office to illustrate. From my broad recollection, the ward timetable from over 30 years ago looked something like this:

Daily tasks (to be carried out each day, including weekends)

7.30 am	Get patients up and dressed
8.30 am	Breakfast
9.00 am	Medication round
9.30–11.30 am	Patients washed and shaved
	Beds made
	Toileting (all patients taken to sit on the toilet)
11.30 am	Cup of tea
12.30 pm	Lunch
1.30 pm	Wash hands and faces
	Medication round
2.30–4.00 pm	Exercise, leisure and visiting time
4.00 pm	Cup of tea
4.30 pm	Toileting
5.30 pm	Medication round
6.00 pm	Evening meal
7.30 pm	Cup of Ovaltine/warm milk
8.30 pm	Toileting

9.30 pm	Medication round
10.00 pm	Bed

All nurses were expected to help with mealtimes and assist patients out of bed in the morning. The remaining jobs were allocated at the start of each shift to individual nurses. On my first day on Fullwood Ward the task assigned to me was 'washes and shaves' so my initial hours in the asylum were spent in the bathroom armed with a flannel and a wet razor-grappling with the craggy faces of 38 old gentlemen, most of whom reacted as if I was Sweeney Todd trying to slit their throats.

Additional tasks were scheduled for particular times of the week. Monday and Friday afternoons were devoted to bathing. At these times the ward residents were ferried in shifts to the bathroom where they were undressed and stood, naked, waiting to be given access to one of the three pre-prepared baths. The three baths were located side by side, without any screens or curtains that would have provided a degree of privacy.

If bath times were undignified, Wednesday afternoons witnessed depravity. The senior nurse offered a rationale.

'Many of the patients are prone to constipation, a serious condition that can cause further confusion and agitation. Their brain defects prevent them from telling us that they're bunged up, so each Wednesday at 2.00 pm we nurses have to give their bowels a helping hand.'

Some weeks later, when allocated to 'bowel care', I discovered that the senior nurse's description of the task was a literal one. At the prescribed time a random sample of the residents was led to a bed (protected with a plastic sheet) at the far end of the dormitory adjacent to two strategically placed commodes. After removing trousers and undergarments, each patient was positioned on his left side on the bed. Pulling on his latex gloves, the senior nurse talked me through the remainder of the procedure.

'First we need to check out how compacted the patient is by inserting a finger into the anus. If progress of the finger meets firm resistance, the hard faeces responsible for the obstruction needs to be removed manually.'

'And if the faeces aren't hard?' I asked, anticipating a reprieve for the unfortunate patient.

'Then we administer a phosphate enema, wait five minutes and sit the patient on the commode.'

So once selected for the bowel-care session, the most favourable outcome awaiting a resident of Fullwood Ward in 1981 was to have 200 millilitres of warm fluid squirted into his rectum.

Fullwood Ward housed patients who suffered organic brain deficits in the form of dementias or other neurological conditions. In contrast, the majority of the asylum residents, those deemed to be mentally ill, had intact brains (apart from those ill-fated patients inflicted with frontal leucotomies, the scars on their temples testimony to the brain mutilation conducted under the guise of therapeutic intervention). These patients resided on the 'long-stay' wards. Here too, routine and order were paramount, sometimes to an absurd degree.

sock-change at noon

The phone rang in the ward nursing office.

'I need you to provide trained cover for Clifton Ward, 12 till 1, to allow the nurse-in-charge to have a lunch break,' said the Nursing Officer, my line manager.

The year was 1985 and, having recently qualified as a Registered Mental Nurse, I could now be trusted with the keys to the drug cabinet and take charge of a ward. As is the case today, policy dictated that there had to be at least one trained nurse on each ward at all times.

I had not been on Clifton Ward before. The nurse-in-charge, en route for the canteen, met me at the door. 'Everything's sorted; there's nothing for you to do. I'll be back about 1 o'clock,' he said, while handing me the drug-cupboard keys.

I entered the main day area of the ward where about two dozen middle-aged gentlemen were sitting at square tables, four patients to each, eating their meals. Two nursing assistants observed from behind the stainless steel food trolley, one nodding in my direction in recognition of my arrival. It was silent apart from the pitter-patter of metal cutlery on plastic plates. By 12.30 most of the patients were munching their jam roly-poly and custard. One of the nursing assistants left the dining area and returned with two cloth bags, one full and one empty, and dropped them beside the tables.

'Sock change!' he shouted.

All of the patients, many with full mouths, turned their chairs away from the table and began removing their socks. Two bare-footed patients left the table and strode towards the bags. One of them (who I later learned had the title 'the sock man') gathered the full bag and handed out a fresh pair of socks to each of his fellow residents seated at the dining table. The other ('the sweaty-sock man') collected the empty bag and held it out in front of each patient so they could drop their old socks into it. The two sock monitors returned the bags to the nursing assistant and rejoined their peers at the table to finish their puddings.

Twiddling the keys in my hand, I watched proceedings in disbelief. In the asylum there is a time and place for everything; on Clifton Ward, 12.30 pm on a Friday was sock-change time!

conformity is king

To survive in the regimented world of the psychiatric asylum required compliance. Expressions of individuality were discouraged. Efficient running of a ward necessitated that inmates adhere to the stringent daily routine. Bathing took place on designated days, and no other. Eating meals and drinking tea were only allowed at prescribed times of day. Denied opportunities to make choices, asylum patients typically became dependent upon instruction of what to do and when to do it (a mind-set referred to as 'institutionalised').

Years of conforming with the 'one size fits all' asylum culture often rendered patients incapable of expressing their preferences even when given the opportunities to do so. While the nurse-in-charge of a long-stay ward in 1987, I decided to introduce a modest change to the meal-time routine to encourage individual choice. In the spirit of democratic decision making, the day prior to the proposed change I asked the patients to meet in the day room. With encouragement, the nursing team succeeded in assembling the majority of the 30 male residents in a seated circle.

I attempted to sell them my big idea. 'I've got everyone together because we would like to introduce a change to what happens at meal times. As you all know, we have always used the large teapots and put milk and sugar in them beforehand. As from tomorrow, we would like to offer each of you the choice as to whether you have milk and sugar in your tea.'

'But I like milk and sugar in my tea,' said Tommy, one of the more outspoken patients.

'You will still be able to have milk and sugar in your tea, Tommy,' I replied, 'but you will have to put it in your cup yourself.'

'Can't we just leave things as they are?' asked Bertie, hands trembling due to the side effects of his antipsychotic medication, and perhaps contemplating whether he could muster the necessary dexterity.

'Some gentlemen on the ward might prefer to drink their tea without milk or sugar,' I said. 'So don't you think they should have the choice?'

My question met with silence. Some patients gazed at their feet, others peered beyond me; no one made eye contact.

'How about we try to do things differently for a couple of weeks, and see how it goes? As from breakfast tomorrow, we will use a small teapot, a milk jug and sugar bowl on each table so people can decide for themselves what they put into their tea. What do you think?'

Silence.

'Shall we give it a go?'

Silence, but a couple of patients nodded, motivated (I suspected) more by a desire to end the ward meeting than in support of the suggested innovation.

At breakfast the next morning the tables, each seating four patients, were supplied with separate teapots, milk jugs and sugar bowls. The usual frenzied grapple for tea did not happen. Instead, each of the quartets stared, motionless, at the novel items in front of them. A rare hush descended upon the dining area of Earby Ward. Tommy then lurched for the teapot, removed the lid, tipped in all the milk and sugar, and poured himself a cup while splashing tea over the table in the process. Despite my protestations, his bold action had a ripple effect, each of the tables replicating the urgent manoeuvre. Having slurped ready-made sweet and milky tea for many years, the gentlemen of Earby Ward were not receptive to the half-baked innovations of a young charge nurse.

the cigarette butt

Isolated from much of the outside world, the asylum population often evolved its own internal structure. At the Prestwich Asylum in the 1980s, although the in-house farm had closed, the hospital grounds incorporated a café, shops, a social club and an industrial unit offering paid employment to inmates in return for producing rustic garden furniture. Such a self-contained environment meant there was little incentive for the inmates to interact with the wider community, and the isolation led to the asylum population developing distinctive customs and practices, one of which was an inherent power hierarchy.

Almost all the inmates smoked and cigarettes were always in demand. The alpha males on Earby Ward worked full time in the industrial units and bought their own cigarettes, whereas the lower-functioning (and less powerful) patients had their supply regulated by the nursing staff. In this community, resources conveyed influence, as did physical strength and aggression. A memorable occasion on Earby Ward, involving the journey of a cigarette butt, demonstrated the power hierarchy that existed within the asylum.

It was early evening and I was standing behind the drug trolley, administering the prescribed medications. The procedure was that I would shout a patient's name, who would then approach the trolley to collect his tablets and swallow them in front of me (to ensure the chemicals were consumed rather than being spat out as soon as the patient was out of the nurse's line of vision). Within two minutes of starting the drug round, Bob (an alpha male) strolled onto the ward, removed a 20-packet of Embassy and box of matches from the inside breast pocket of his jacket, lit himself a cigarette and puffed away while leaning on a radiator. The other patients observed from a distance, no one daring to encroach within an implicit three-metre 'no go' area around him.

Having smoked half the length of the cigarette, Bob sauntered across the day room towards a group of onlookers, each of whom were staring, hardly breathing, at the lit cigarette. Having taken one last drag, he handed it to Joe, the second-in-command, who strode towards a quieter corner of the room, four of his peers in pursuit. As Joe puffed, the others encroached within touching distance, asking for the cigarette stub but stopping short of any physical contact. With less than one inch of the cigarette remaining, Joe flicked it onto the floor in the direction of the four observers. A skirmish ensued, with Tommy exiting the scrum victorious, a burning ember between his lips.

At this moment I shouted Tommy's name to collect his medication. With frustration etched on his face at my lousy timing, he approached the drug trolley and, after some deliberation, he balanced the stub on the edge of the metal shelf underneath the trolley and proceeded to swallow his tranquillisers. Within an instant of his putting the stub down, I noticed movement in my peripheral vision. Danny, a patient with learning difficulties and perpetual agitation who was near the bottom of the pecking order, was accelerating towards us. When he reached the trolley he swooped like a Spitfire and plucked from the shelf what remained of the glowing stub, evading Tommy's swipes in the process. By the time Tommy reached him, the ember had burnt itself out on Danny's protruding bottom lip, an emerging blister the only remaining evidence that it had existed.

2

an illness like any other?

part I: where it all went wrong

The 'illness like any other' mantra is often espoused by psychiatric professionals and psychiatric organisations across the developed world to support their assertion that the last 150 years have witnessed impressive progress in the treatment of mental disorders. The American National Institute of Mental Health, the largest research organisation in the world specialising in mental disorders, boldly claims in its introductory information that, 'Depressive illnesses are disorders of the brain' (NIMH, 2014a) and 'Schizophrenia is a chronic, severe, and disabling brain disorder' (NIMH, 2014b). The huge advocacy group in the USA, the National Alliance on Mental Illness, broadcasts that 'Just as diabetes is a disorder of the pancreas, mental illnesses are medical conditions …' (NAMI, 2014).

The assertion that mental disorders are primarily caused by biological aberrations, and are therefore analogous to physical illnesses like diabetes, is the source of much that is wrong with current psychiatric practice. Part I of this chapter will provide a concise overview of the empirical research purporting to support the 'illness like any other' argument, followed by a critique of this literature. Part II will provide actual clinical vignettes to illustrate how this fallacious assumption encourages psychiatric practices that are disadvantageous to service users.

early biological explanations

The earliest biological explanations of madness emerged in the fifth century CE and represented a step forward from the prevailing assumption that sufferers were possessed by demons. Hippocrates, the most famous physician of all time, proposed that a person's mental health was determined by the balance of four humours (black bile, yellow bile, phlegm and blood). In what represents the first biochemical-imbalance theory of mental disorder, Hippocrates believed that illness was caused by an abundance or deficiency of one or more of the humours; for example, a surplus of black bile was thought to induce depression. The balance-of-humours theory was simple and seductive, easily understood by the layperson, yet open to further elaboration by the expert medical practitioner. The parallels with modern-day biological explanations of psychiatric disorders are striking.

Another early biological model of madness was proposed in the thirteenth century when a professor of theology, Bartholomaeus, described how mental illness had natural causes (not supernatural ones). In the *Encyclopaedia of Bartholomaeus the Englishman* (cited in Clare, 1980, p. 50), a comprehensive treatise on the natural sciences, he proposed that madness was caused by disturbances in specific parts of the brain.

A similar argument linking brain morphology to character, thoughts and emotions was advanced by physician Franz Joseph Gall in the early nineteenth century. Gall developed the science of phrenology based on the premise that the size and shape of areas of the brain determined the range of mental activities. According to phrenologists, measurement of the skull can predict a person's temperament and functioning.

the mission to discover a biological cause

The rapid advances in technology and biochemistry in the second half of the twentieth century spawned more sophisticated procedures for revealing the internal structure of the brain. No longer limited to abstract speculation or interpreting the size of head bumps, the search for discrete brain pathology that causes mental illness – the holy grail of biological psychiatry – was the focus of frenetic investigation.

The research assault on the human brain examined anatomical, biochemical and functional differences between the mentally ill and those without such disorders.

anatomical abnormalities

Over the last 40 years, techniques to reveal the intricacies of brain structure have become increasingly refined. These technological advances culminated in the development of magnetic resonance imaging (MRI), which uses a combination of magnetic fields and radio waves to produce high-quality, three-dimensional images of the brain.

Patients diagnosed with schizophrenia (a mental disorder characterised by voice hearing, unusual beliefs and jumbled thoughts) have typically been targeted by investigators striving to demonstrate structural differences between their brains and those of non-sufferers. An early finding of such studies was that the lateral ventricles (fluid-filled cavities in the brain) were larger in those people with schizophrenia (Johnstone et al., 1976).

Subsequent MRI studies found that brain abnormalities in schizophrenia sufferers were not restricted to the lateral ventricles, structural differences being highlighted in many other areas of the brain including the temporal lobes (associated with emotion regulation and memory) and the frontal lobes (associated with higher-level intellectual functions, including speech) (Shenton et al., 2000).

biochemical abnormalities

The hunt for biochemical imbalances as a cause of mental illness has centred on the levels of neurotransmitters – substances responsible for conducting messages from one brain cell (neurone) to another. Much of the research effort has striven to detect an aberration in a neurotransmitter that could account for the emergence of schizophrenia. One neurotransmitter, dopamine, has attracted enormous interest.

It has long been recognised that amphetamines and other stimulant drugs can trigger psychotic states in some individuals (Curran, Byrappa & McBride, 2004). As amphetamines are known to enhance dopamine production in the brain, the premise that excessive dopamine can cause schizophrenia gained widespread currency.

Further arguments in support of dopamine overactivity as a forerunner to schizophrenia have derived from an understanding of the mechanism of action of drugs used to treat it. Since the 1950s the dominant clinical intervention for schizophrenia has been antipsychotic medications which, for many patients, effectively dampen psychotic symptoms such as voice hearing and paranoia. Most antipsychotics reduce dopamine activity in the brain, thereby suggesting this neurotransmitter might have some aetiological role in schizophrenia.

Neurotransmitters conduct messages from one brain cell to another by connecting with a corresponding receptor on the target cell. The discovery, at postmortem, that there is a proliferation of dopamine receptors in the brains of schizophrenia sufferers has further implicated excess dopamine as a causative factor.

A similar line of reasoning resulted in another neurotransmitter, serotonin, being proposed as a cause of depression (Coppen, 1967). Two types of antidepressant medication, monoamine oxidase inhibitors (MAOIs for short) and the tricyclics, augment the amount of serotonin transmitting messages between brain cells. If depression can be countered by stimulating production of serotonin, it has been argued that a lack of serotonin might be the biochemical imbalance underpinning the disorder.

neuropsychological abnormalities

Another method of investigating the integrity of the brain is to assess a person's cognitive and intellectual abilities by administering a battery of assessments, typically involving a combination of general knowledge questions, memory tests and visual puzzles. These approaches, known within psychiatric services as neuropsychological assessments, provide a way of inferring organic defects without direct observation of brain structure.

Neuropsychological testing of children and adolescents has led researchers to propose that verbal-skills deficits (Jones et al., 1994) and low intelligence (or IQ) (Davidson et al., 1999) independently predict a diagnosis of schizophrenia in adulthood.

the mission to discover a genetic disease

While biological psychiatry researchers were scouring brains for defects that might cause schizophrenia, a parallel strand of frenetic endeavour strove to demonstrate that schizophrenia was a genetically inherited brain disease.

twin studies

If schizophrenia was a genetic disease, passed from one generation to another, the study of identical twins seemed to offer an ideal opportunity to prove it. Genes are the blueprints for our biological constitution, and each of us inherits half of our genes from each parent, so siblings (including non-identical twins) have about 50 per cent of their genetic material in common. Identical twins are formed when a fertilised egg splits into two while in the womb, resulting in the unique circumstance where two people possess identical genes. By calculating concordance rates (the degree to which family members are similarly afflicted by schizophrenia) many researchers have declared support for a genetic cause. If schizophrenia is genetically determined, the argument is that the concordance rate will correspond to the proportion of genes that are shared – identical twins having very high concordance, siblings and non-identical twins an intermediate level, while more distant relatives would display low concordance.

Genetic research into mental illness surfaced in the 1930s when German psychiatrists, sympathetic to the Nazi cause, were the driving force behind legislation that led to the compulsory sterilisation of psychiatric patients and, subsequently, the extermination of 70,000 of the residents in Germany's mental institutions (Meyer, 1988). In 1946 Franz Kallmann, a student of the protagonists in this dark era in psychiatry's history, published a large study in which he had found an 86 per cent schizophrenia-concordance rate for identical twins compared to only 15 per cent for non-identical twins (Kallmann, 1946).

Another famous investigation reported the schizophrenia concordance rate for *four* women with identical genes (Rosenthal & Quinn, 1977). Referred to by American researchers as the Genain quadruplets (the term 'Genain' being a derivative of a Greek word meaning 'dreadful gene') the four identical sisters were all said to suffer from schizophrenia. It was calculated that such concordance could only occur by chance once in over one billion births and therefore represented strong evidence for viewing schizophrenia as a genetic brain disease.

adoption studies

Another approach to investigating the degree to which genes contribute to the development of schizophrenia has been to calculate the concordance rate between adopted children and their biological parents. Influential studies in the 1970s (Rosenthal et al., 1971; Kety et al., 1976) utilised Denmark's comprehensive adoption records to explore the rates of schizophrenia in children of schizophrenic mothers who had been adopted away at a young age. A parallel strand of investigation identified a cohort of adults with a current diagnosis of schizophrenia who had been adopted as children, and traced their biological parents to determine what proportion had also been identified as schizophrenia sufferers. These studies calculated a greater concordance rate for schizophrenia in adoptees who had similarly afflicted parents as compared to adoptees who had mentally healthy parents.

The authors of a number of other adoption studies have all concluded that their results supported important genetic contributions to the development of schizophrenia (for review, see Joseph, 2013). By reporting higher-than-expected schizophrenia concordance rates between mothers and their adopted-away children, these investigations appeared to effectively distinguish genetic influences from those of the environment; if a child of a schizophrenic mother is at greater risk of developing schizophrenia even when adopted away as a baby, this seems convincing evidence of a genetic aetiology.

a critique of the evidence supporting a biological cause

The body of evidence claiming to support a primary biological basis for schizophrenia is often regurgitated in traditional textbooks of psychiatry, and it would be easy to assume that the validity of the 'illness like any other' assertion had been proven beyond reasonable doubt. This is not so. Upon closer inspection, the evidence touted as indicative of mental illness being a genetic brain disease is so riddled with flaws and biases as to render it unconvincing.

brain abnormalities: cause or consequence?

The demonstration of structural and biochemical differences in the brains of people with mental illness as compared to the general population does not establish these differences as causal. Other explanations, at least as plausible as those advocated by biological researchers, could account for these brain abnormalities.

Studies purporting to show brain abnormalities in schizophrenia sufferers often have failed to control for the eventuality that these aberrations are the consequences of psychiatric treatments rather than causative factors. Long-term use of antipsychotic medication has been shown to accelerate the production of dopamine receptors in the brain (Murugaiah et al., 1982) and could therefore account for their abundance in postmortem brains of schizophrenia sufferers. This medication-induced proliferation in dopamine receptors could also explain why many psychosis sufferers relapse when their medication is withdrawn, a phenomenon almost always interpreted by psychiatric services as a 'return of the illness' and the equivalent of a diabetes sufferer deteriorating after ceasing to take insulin.

Further evidence that excess dopamine in people with a schizophrenia diagnosis may be a consequence of their treatment comes from the failure to find overactivity in the dopamine systems at postmortem in psychosis sufferers who had not been on antipsychotic medication (Haracz, 1982).

More recent neuro-imaging studies have cast doubt on whether dopamine activity is indeed elevated in patients diagnosed with schizophrenia, a review reporting that 11 out of 13 studies failed to find increased dopamine receptor density in the clinical groups (Copolov & Crook, 2000).

Long-term use of antipsychotic medication may also contribute to the development of some of the reported structural changes in the brains of schizophrenia sufferers, one author describing the drug-induced neurological consequences for patients as a 'plague of brain damage' (Breggin, 1991).

brain abnormalities: alternative explanations

The concerted research effort to discover a primary biological basis for schizophrenia has habitually failed to consider the possibility that environmental factors might contribute to the development of the disorder. The investigators involved in studies claiming to have found evidence for biological causation seem, for the most part, to betray a pre-existing conviction that schizophrenia is a brain disease and it is inevitable that biochemical and neuronal aberrations will be discovered. Such a bias has led to the premature conclusion that any identified differences between the brains of the mentally disordered and the non-afflicted must be causal; alternative explanations have often not even been considered.

The shape and composition of the human brain can be influenced by many factors, including age, ethnicity, level of educational attainment and physical health status, all of which have to be considered when interpreting the results of anatomical and biochemical studies. A greater challenge to valid interpretation is the coexistence of alcohol and drug misuse, behaviours that are recognised to be elevated within mentally disordered populations and which could independently account for any identified brain abnormalities.

The most crucial omission endemic within biological research into schizophrenia is the failure to consider the role of traumatic life experiences in the development of the disorder. Crucially, there is compelling evidence that childhood victimisation (a phenomenon that is commonly reported by psychosis sufferers) can alter both brain structure and neurotransmitter pathways (Kaufman & Carney, 2001). It is therefore plausible that any discrepancies between the brains of people with mental illness and healthy controls are primarily the result of childhood trauma rather than representing an inherited defect that causes mental disorder.

neuropsychological deficits: lack of specificity

John Forbes Nash, a schizophrenia sufferer and Nobel Prize-winning mathematician, whose life was portrayed in the film *A Beautiful Mind*, demonstrated that it was possible to be both highly intelligent and mentally ill. Further doubt on the premise that intellectual and verbal deficits might confer vulnerability to schizophrenia comes from the failure to find any significant association between cognitive ability and the prevalence of psychotic symptoms in 1,500 patients with a schizophrenia diagnosis (Keefe et al., 2006).

the exaggeration of the genetic contribution

Books addressing genetic contributions to psychiatric disorders typically assert that schizophrenia is 80 per cent determined by a person's genes (Jang, 2005). Although genetics clearly influence whether or not someone will develop symptoms that will attract a diagnosis of schizophrenia, the research purporting to demonstrate genetic causation is riddled with biases ranging from flagrant manipulation of data to subtle statistical manoeuvres.

loose definitions

Already convinced that schizophrenia was a genetically inherited brain disease, some researchers have applied flexible definitions of key concepts so as to ensure that the outcomes support genetic causation (Joseph, 2013).

Determining whether a person meets the criteria for schizophrenia has always been an unreliable process, and some often-quoted twin studies have been guilty of using self-serving definitions of the disorder. Investigators initially involved in studying the Genain identical quadruplets labelled all four as schizophrenic despite these four troubled women displaying disparate difficulties. Closer inspection of the quadruplets revealed marked variation in both the type and intensity of their problems (Bentall, 2009, pp. 116–17). A similar stretching of the diagnostic criteria for schizophrenia was evident in the Danish–American twin studies (Rosenthal et al., 1971) where the authors adopted the broader variable 'schizophrenia spectrum disorder' to guarantee findings consistent with a genetic aetiology (Bentall, 2009, p. 124).

Similarly, in the Kallmann (1946) study the author judged which cases were to be labelled 'schizophrenic' without recourse to formal diagnostic criteria. Furthermore, whether twins were identical or non-identical was determined by visual inspection, genetic testing having yet to be developed. Such potential biases can account for the inflated figure of 86 per cent schizophrenia concordance rates for identical twins reported in the study.

statistical biases

Genetic researchers use the term 'heritability' as a measure of the genetic contribution to a particular disorder. Calculated from concordance rates in family, twin and adoption studies, heritability for schizophrenia of 80 per cent or more has been the typical figure quoted.

The concept of heritability skews conclusions in favour of genetic contributions to schizophrenia via two statistical tricks. Firstly, concordance rates have often been amplified by calculating them in a way that is counterintuitive. A common-sense approach (referred to as the 'pairwise' approach) would count participants only once; so if a study traced eight schizophrenia sufferers who had an identical twin, and found that four of them had a similarly afflicted twin, the study would conclude a 50 per cent concordance rate. Instead, many genetic researchers adopt a 'probandwise' approach which counts participants twice by calculating the proportion of schizophrenia sufferers in the cohort who have an affected twin; in the above example eight of the twelve have a concordant twin so the cited concordance rate would be 67 per cent.

Secondly, when counting the number of relatives of schizophrenia sufferers who are similarly afflicted, genetic researchers often 'correct for age' by assuming a percentage of the younger participants will become schizophrenic in the future. Such a statistical manoeuvre would not be used in research exploring environmental contributions to the emergence of psychosis.

In addition to biases involved in its calculation, estimates of heritability are commonly misinterpreted as indicating the percentage cause of a disorder – so if heritability for schizophrenia is calculated to be 80 per cent, the common inference is that genes are 80 per cent responsible for the development of schizophrenia. What heritability actually measures is the percentage of *variation* in a disorder that originates from genes; if there is little or no variation in the environment, heritability will always be high. Bentall cogently illustrates this point with the example that, if everyone in the world smoked 20 cigarettes per day, heritability for lung cancer would be almost 100 per cent with genetic vulnerability totally explaining why some smokers get the disease while others do not (Bentall, 2009, p. 126).

Scholarly reviews of the genetic research literature that have excluded the effects of these methodological flaws and focused only on more recent, better-designed studies have estimated the schizophrenia concordance rate for identical twins and non-identical twins to be 22 per cent and 5 per cent respectively (Joseph, 2013), indicative of a real but relatively modest genetic contribution.

the equivalent environment myth

The validity of the conclusion of a genetic contribution to the development of schizophrenia on the basis that identical twin concordance rates are greater than those for non-identical twins crucially depends on the assumption that the family environments of these two cohorts are the same. There is evidence to suggest this is not the case, identical twins experiencing more similar social and physical environments than their non-identical counterparts (Joseph, 1998). The twin studies claiming to support the premise that schizophrenia is a genetic brain disease are, therefore, confounded by environmental influences.

The adoption studies strived to exclude the potential environmental effects and, on first reading, seem to provide stronger evidence for genetic contributions to schizophrenia. By demonstrating that children of schizophrenic mothers continued to be at greater risk of developing schizophrenia themselves despite being adopted away as babies, the adoption studies are often considered to be convincing evidence of a genetic aetiology. Yet closer inspection reveals a series of methodological weaknesses.

As with the twin studies (discussed above) the adoption-study researchers were often guilty of using loose definitions of schizophrenia and making snap diagnostic judgements based on limited information. Occasionally, interviews with participants seemed to have been fabricated (Joseph, 2013).

In addition, the adoption studies did not achieve their central goal of adequately controlling for environmental influences. Many late adoptees were included in the samples, thereby exposing children to their schizophrenic mothers before their adoptions took place. Also, it seems unlikely that the two groups of adoptees (those from schizophrenic mothers and those from healthy controls) had an equal chance of being placed into the range of adoptive homes, those children tainted with a mental illness background presumably being less desirable adoptees in countries (Finland, Denmark and the USA) that all had eugenic laws throughout the periods the adoptions had taken place. Given these prevalent attitudes towards the mentally ill in the early and middle parts of the twentieth century, it is difficult to believe that the most resourced adoptive parents would not have preferentially selected children from non-mentally ill parentage.

the importance of life experience

Researchers wedded to the view that severe mental illness is a genetic brain disease have consistently ignored the possibility that life experiences might substantially influence whether or not a person will develop these disorders. When challenged to consider environmental factors their response has been either to attempt, unsuccessfully, to control for it (for example, the twin and adoption studies) or to estimate environmental contributions by exclusion (for example, by erroneously claiming that if the heritability for schizophrenia is 80 per cent the life-experience component can be no more than 20 per cent).

In order to achieve a valid estimation of the role of life experience in the development of schizophrenia, each environmental factor of interest must be investigated in its own right. When such research has been conducted, the findings have supported the premise that a person's life experiences are important determinants of mental illness. Two striking examples are childhood trauma and the emotional intensity within the family milieu.

Childhood sexual abuse has been shown to render a person 15 times more susceptible to psychosis in adulthood when compared to someone who has not suffered these experiences (Bebbington et al., 2004). The magnitude of this effect is in excess of any gene as yet discovered.

For over half a century it has been recognised that psychosis sufferers are more likely to relapse if they return to a home environment that is characterised by criticism, hostility or emotional over-involvement. Collectively known in the research literature as 'expressed emotion', a comprehensive review of studies in this area concluded that high levels of these features within the home was a significant and robust predictor of relapse in schizophrenia (as well as a range of other psychiatric disorders) (Butzlaff & Hooley, 1998).

The question of whether family environments contribute to the *onset* of schizophrenia has been actively avoided by researchers because of concerns that this line of investigation might be perceived as blaming parents. It is implausible that high expressed emotion could be such a potent trigger for schizophrenic relapse yet not have any aetiological role, and researchers that have ventured into this taboo area have accrued strong evidence that the quality of the interpersonal environment contributes significantly to the emergence of the disorder (for a review, see Read & Seymour, 2013). Of particular note is a prospective study (Doane et al., 1981; Goldstein, 1987) that followed up 64 troubled (but non-psychotic) teenagers over a 15-year period; this found that three specific characteristics of the family milieu at the start of the study independently predicted a diagnosis of schizophrenia in adulthood. The three predictors were: high expressed emotion; an affective style displaying criticism, guilt-induction and intrusiveness; and parental communication deviance, involving a tendency to speak in a way that militates against a shared understanding.

the disadvantages of an 'illness like any other' approach

A critical review of the evidence has shown that there is little to support biological psychiatry's fundamental assertion that schizophrenia is a genetically transmitted brain disease. But what are the consequences of adhering to an 'illness like any other' approach?

The obsession with presuming a biological cause of mental illness has, throughout history, led to many atrocities being committed by the psychiatric profession under the guise of treatment (Sidley, 2012). These have included: use of leeches, laxatives and emetics to rid the body of insanity-causing fluids; physical assaults, including immersion in cold water and the application of red-hot pokers simultaneously to the head and feet; genital mutilation; surgical removal of teeth, testicles, ovaries and colon; inducing comas via the repeated injection of insulin; brain mutilation (referred to as leucotomy); triggering epileptic seizures by means of electric shocks; and gross overuse of medication. Although most of these 'treatments' are now extinct, electric shock and excessive drug prescribing continue to be widespread within our current psychiatric system.

Subsequent chapters will address a range of disadvantages for service users that follow from Western psychiatry's stubborn persistence with the 'illness like any other' approach. These will include: the encouragement of passivity; disabling side effects of interventions; the discrimination against some forms of human distress; the crushing of hope; and a degree of risk aversion that regularly stifles the opportunities for therapeutic progress. In addition, the entrenched propensity for psychiatrists and most other health professionals to regard mental health problems as synonymous with physical illnesses contaminates their routine interactions with, and understandings of, service users. The second part of this chapter will provide real examples of this poisonous process in action within contemporary psychiatric services.

references

Bebbington, P.E., Bhugra, D., Brugha, T., Singleton, N., Farrell, M., Jenkins, R. et al. (2004). Psychosis, victimisation and childhood disadvantage: Evidence from the second British National Survey of Psychiatric Morbidity. *British Journal of Psychiatry, 185*, 220–6.

Bentall, R.P. (2009). *Doctoring the Mind: Why psychiatric treatments fail.* London: Allen Lane.

Breggin, P.R. (1991). *Toxic Psychiatry: Why therapy, empathy and love must replace the drugs, electroshock and biochemical theories of the 'new psychiatry'.* New York: St Martin's Press.

Butzlaff, R.L. & Hooley, J.M. (1998). Expressed emotion and psychiatric relapse: A meta-analysis. *Archives of General Psychiatry, 55*(6), 547–52.

Clare, A. (1980). *Psychiatry in Dissent: Controversial issues in thought and practice* (2nd ed.). London: Tavistock Publications.

Copolov, D. & Crook, J. (2000). Biological markers and schizophrenia. *Australian and New Zealand Journal of Psychiatry, 34* (suppl.), S108–12.

Coppen, A. (1967). The biochemistry of affective disorders. *British Journal of Psychiatry, 113*, 1237–64.

Curran, C., Byrappa, N. & McBride, A. (2004). Stimulant psychosis: Systematic review. *British Journal of Psychiatry, 185*, 196–204.

Davidson, M., Reichenberg, A., Rabinowitz, J., Weiser, M., Kaplan, Z. & Mark, M. (1999). Behavioral and intellectual markers for schizophrenia in apparently healthy male adolescents. *American Journal of Psychiatry, 156*, 1328–35.

Doane, J.A., West, K.L., Goldstein, M.J., Rodnick, E.H. & Jones, J.E. (1981). Parental communication deviance and affective style: Predictors of subsequent schizophrenia spectrum disorders in vulnerable adolescents. *Archives of General Psychiatry, 38*(6), 679–85.

Goldstein, M. (1987). The UCLA High-Risk Project. *Schizophrenia Bulletin, 13*, 505–14.

Haracz, J. (1982). The dopamine hypothesis. *Schizophrenia Bulletin, 8*, 438–69.

Jang, K.L. (2005). *The Behavioral Genetics of Psychopathology.* Mahwah, NJ: Erlbaum.

Johnstone, E.C., Crow, T.J., Frith, C.D., Husband, J. & Kreel, L. (1976). Cerebral ventricular size and cognitive impairment in chronic schizophrenia. *Lancet, 2*, 924–6.

Jones, P.B., Rodgers, B., Murray, R.M. & Marmot, M. (1994). Child development risk factors for adult schizophrenia in the British 1946 birth cohort. *Lancet, 344*, 1398–402.

Joseph, J. (1998). The equal environment assumption of the classical twin method: A critical analysis. *Journal of Mind and Behavior, 19,* 325–58.

Joseph, J. (2013). 'Schizophrenia' and heredity: Why the emperor (still) has no genes. In J. Read & J. Dillon (Eds.), *Models of Madness: Psychological, social and biological approaches to schizophrenia* (2nd ed.; pp. 72–89). London: Routledge.

Kallmann, F.J. (1946). The genetic theory of schizophrenia: An analysis of 691 schizophrenic twin index families. *American Journal of Psychiatry, 103*(3), 309–22.

Kaufman, J. & Carney, D. (2001). Effects of early stress on brain structure and function: Implications for understanding the relationship between child maltreatment and depression. *Development and Psychopathology, 13,* 451–71.

Keefe, R.S., Bilder, R.M., Harvey, P.D., Davis, S.M., Palmer, B.W., Gold, J.M., et al. (2006). Baseline neurocognitive deficits in the CATIE schizophrenia trial. *Neuropsychopharmacology, 31,* 2033–46.

Kety, S.S., Rosenthal, D., Wender, P.H., Schulsinger, F. & Jacobsen, B. (1976). Mental illness in the biological and adoptive families of adopted individuals who have become schizophrenic. *Behavior Genetics, 6,* 219–25.

Meyer, J.E. (1988). The fate of the mentally ill in Germany during the Third Reich. *Psychological Medicine, 18,* 575–81.

Murugaiah, K., Theodorou, A., Mann, S., Clow, A., Jenner, P. & Marsden, C.D. (1982). Chronic continuous administration of neuroleptic drugs alters cerebral dopamine receptors and increases spontaneous dopaminergic action in the striatum. *Nature, 296,* 570–2.

National Alliance on Mental Illness (NAMI). (2014). *Mental Illnesses.* Retrieved 21 April 2014 from http://www.nami.org/Template.cfm?Section=By_Illness

National Institute of Mental Health (NIMH). (2014a). *Depression.* Retrieved 21 April 2014 from http://www.nimh.nih.gov/health/topics/depression/index.shtml

National Institute of Mental Health (NIMH). (2014b). *Schizophrenia.* Retrieved 21 April 2014 from http://www.nimh.nih.gov/health/topics/schizophrenia/index.shtml

Read, J. & Seymour, F. (2013). Psychosis and families: Intergenerational parenting problems. In J. Read & J. Dillon (Eds.), *Models of Madness: Psychological, social and biological approaches to schizophrenia* (2nd ed.; pp. 276–91). London: Routledge.

Rosenthal, D. & Quinn, O.W. (1977). Quadruplet hallucinations: Phenotypic variations of a schizophrenic genotype. *Archives of General Psychiatry, 34,* 817–27.

Rosenthal, D., Wender, P.H., Kety, S.S., Welner, J. & Schulsinger, F. (1971). The adopted-away offspring of schizophrenics. *American Journal of Psychiatry*, *128*, 307–11.

Shenton, M.E., Dickey, C.C., Frumin, M. & McCarley, R.W. (2000). A review of MRI findings in schizophrenia. *Schizophrenia Research*, *49*, 1–52.

Sidley, G.L. (2012). *Psychiatric Atrocities: 10 shameful interventions inflicted on the mentally ill.* Retrieved 22 April 2014 from http://gsidley.hubpages.com/hub/Psychiatric-atrocities-the-10-most-shameful-things-doctors-have-done-under-the-guise-of-treating-mental-illness

part II: the pernicious assumption
of underlying deficits

'but he's got schizophrenia!'

'It's my legs; I keep getting this funny feeling in my legs,' said Colin, gazing at the floor.

Colin had been in the interview room with me for 10 minutes and, prior to this point, had responded to each of my questions with a blank stare and a whispered, 'Don't know'. It was my first meeting with Colin. In my role as a clinical psychologist within a community mental health team, I had been asked to see him by a psychiatric-nurse colleague who, recognising Colin's lack of improvement, was seeking ideas as to how we might enable progress to be made with his mental health problems.

Two further one-hour meetings with Colin, supplemented by a thorough reading of his clinical record, revealed that he had been in receipt of numerous treatments. Colin was 40 years old and had been a psychiatric patient for over two decades. In his late teens his parents had witnessed him talking to himself in his bedroom, shouting for no apparent reason and, when questioned, responding with incoherent answers. The psychiatrist who assessed him in 1990 diagnosed 'paranoid schizophrenia' and prescribed chlorpromazine (a drug from a family of chemicals known as neuroleptics that function to reduce psychotic symptoms, such as voice hearing and delusional beliefs).

Over the subsequent 22 years within the psychiatric system Colin followed the recommendations of the doctors and ingested multiple antipsychotic tablets and syrups (haloperidol, promazine, pimozide, thioridazine and sulpiride) and had antipsychotic chemicals, otherwise known as 'depot' medications (Depixol, Clopixol and Piportil), injected into his buttocks. He had never been involved in any important relationships and continued to live with his elder sister.

There had been two previous attempts to engage Colin in psychological therapy, both of which were abandoned owing to his poor concentration and his manifest difficulty in maintaining focus on one topic at a time. When I met Colin, he remained on antipsychotic medication in combination with another type of drug, an antidepressant, intended to raise his mood. Despite this combination of drugs, Colin's sister reported that her brother continued to be tormented by his voice hearing and persecutory beliefs, regularly pacing the house in the early hours of the morning, talking to himself and shouting. His suspiciousness extended to psychiatric professionals, at times believing they were poisoning him. Colin's lifestyle was impoverished, without friends, job or leisure activities. All in all, I was struggling to see how our community mental health team might enable Colin to extricate himself from his enduring anguish and isolation.

Faced with such a stalemate, I strived to identify a specific area of Colin's life that he might wish to change, an area sufficiently important to Colin to motivate him to work with us. During my third session with Colin I continued to probe for such a hook, returning to something he had referred to in our first session.

'If there was just one thing you could change about your current life, what would it be?' I asked.

'My legs,' Colin said.

'What is it about your legs you'd like to change?'

Colin stared at the floor. 'My legs feel weird.'

'What do you think is making your legs feel weird?'

'It's the drugs; they make my legs feel queer.'

This was the most coherent sequence of responses that Colin had made during our interviews and seemed something of a breakthrough. Irrespective of whether it was the medications that were responsible for his leg discomfort – given the multiple side effects of antipsychotic drugs, such a link was conceivable – this specific aspect of his experience seemed important to Colin and offered an opportunity to engage him in a collaborative change process.

'So what would you want to do about the drugs?' I asked.

'I don't want to take them anymore,' he said.

'Have you spoken to your psychiatrist, Dr Phillips, about this?'

'Yes, but he doesn't take any notice.'

The following week I met with Dr Phillips and Colin's psychiatric nurse to discuss potential ways forward. I suggested that we should consider adhering to Colin's request. The psychiatrist and the nurse looked at each other and grinned, as if I had suggested something absurd.

'But most nights he is still tormented by his psychotic symptoms,' said the nurse.

'Then maybe the medication is not helping very much,' I said. 'And perhaps, by respecting his request to come off his medication, he might start to work with us to try and improve the quality of his life.'

Dr Phillips sighed, and shook his head while reading Colin's clinical record from the computer screen. 'But he's got schizophrenia; the diagnosis is unequivocal. It would be unethical to take him off his antipsychotics.'

Despite my further representations about the potential benefits of adhering to Colin's wishes, the psychiatric team rejected the idea of weaning him off his antipsychotic medication and Colin continues to endure both recurrent voice-hearing distress and an impoverished life.

I have no doubt that the psychiatrist and community psychiatric nurse acted in what they believed were the best interests of their patient. But the deeply engrained 'illness like any other' notion led them to construe the drug-withdrawal proposal as tantamount to a patient with a definite medical disorder (where a direct and causal link has been demonstrated between biological disturbance and illness) making the irrational request to stop effective treatment. Asking to stop antipsychotics was deemed to be equivalent to a person with insulin-dependent diabetes (where a lack of the hormone, insulin, leads to a life-threatening increase in the amount of glucose in the bloodstream) refusing to accept an injection of insulin; or someone with a rampant, potentially fatal chest infection (where lung-attacking bacteria have been identified) refusing to take antibiotics; or a malaria sufferer, whose body has been invaded by the specific, mosquito-borne micro-organism, refusing to take anti-malarial medication.

if she would only accept the diagnosis

Nineteen-year-old Millie fidgeted in her chair and, despite it being mid-December, droplets of sweat were noticeable on her forehead. The meeting was a Care Programme Approach (CPA) review, an obligatory forum within the psychiatric system where the patient and involved professional staff get together to discuss progress to date and agree a plan of action for the future. Millie had opted to bring her mother with her for support. As well as me, the psychologist, the other professional staff comprised the psychiatrist, community psychiatric nurse and a student psychiatric nurse. Also present was a secretary to take notes of the meeting.

Twelve months prior to this review meeting, Millie had first come into contact with psychiatric services following a psychotic episode while at university. Sexually abused by her stepfather as a child, Millie had always lacked confidence and had difficulty making friends. Despite her isolation, she had achieved good A-level grades, gained entry to university and had left home for the first time. Within four weeks of starting her degree course, a drunken male student had made sexual advances towards her in a pub and had become verbally abusive to Millie when she repelled him. Subsequently, she had suffered nightmares about her childhood sexual abuse and had difficulty sleeping. She had stopped attending her lectures and spent most of the time in her room at the university hall of residence. Her fellow students had become concerned about her when she told them that al-Qaeda terrorists had planted maggots under her skin that were now devouring her internal organs. She had also accused another student of putting arsenic in her food. The details of Millie's deteriorating mental state and bizarre behaviour were reported to the university tutors. Her mother was contacted and she immediately came to collect Millie and take her home.

While back in the family home, Millie continued to express ideas of being poisoned and 'devoured from the inside' by maggots. Following a psychiatric assessment, she was admitted to an inpatient facility where she resided for five weeks. On the day of admission, Millie was prescribed olanzapine (one of a group of newer, 'atypical' antipsychotic medications for the treatment of schizophrenia), but continued to protest about her perceived persecution. After two weeks on the ward, the dose of olanzapine was increased and her distressing beliefs about others doing her harm ceased. At this point she had been diagnosed as having suffered a first episode of schizophrenia. Since discharge from hospital, she had continued to take the olanzapine and her mother reported that she had not expressed any further ideas of persecution, instead appearing withdrawn and dispirited.

During the CPA review the psychiatric nurse summarised the events of the previous few months: how the 'paranoid delusions' had responded well to the olanzapine, and how she had been discussing with Millie the prospect of a gradual return to academic study. Millie had said very little during the meeting. Towards the end of the review the nurse encouraged her to participate in the development of the plan of care for the next few months.

'How do you think things are progressing, Millie?' asked the nurse.

'OK, I suppose,' said Millie.

'Is there anything you would wish to change about the care plan?'

The care plan is a written document outlining what help and interventions will be offered to the patient between now and the next review. Millie's care plan comprised two elements: for the psychiatric nurse to visit fortnightly to monitor mental state and the side effects of the medication; and a crisis number that Millie (or her mother) could ring in the event of a psychiatric emergency. Continued ingestion of the olanzapine was assumed rather than explicitly stated.

'Do I have to keep taking the olanzapine?' asked Millie.

'It is vital that you remain on the medication for at least two years, to prevent the illness coming back,' said the psychiatrist.

Millie squirmed in her chair and looked towards her mother, as if seeking her support.

'What it is,' said the mother, 'is that Millie has always been very conscious of her weight and she is upset that, since going onto the medication, she has put on a few pounds.'

'A few pounds!' said Millie, showing animation for the first time in the meeting, 'Almost a stone and a half.'

Antipsychotic drugs have many unwanted side effects and, because of its impact on a recipient's metabolism, olanzapine commonly leads to considerable weight gain.

'She's never had much confidence in herself,' said mother, 'but she's always kept fit and slim. Yesterday, when she stepped on the weighing scales, she burst into tears. She's read that weight gain is due to her olanzapine. Is there any chance of reducing the dose, or even weaning her off it?'

'We will consider this in due course,' said the psychiatrist, 'but for now she must stay on the medication. Weight gain is a small price to pay for keeping well. Maybe we can provide some dietary advice.'

The next day, in his letter to Millie's doctor summarising the review meeting, the psychiatrist included the statement: 'I get the impression that she and her family still have difficulties accepting the diagnosis.'

Once again, a period of paranoia and irrationality is viewed as an illness with a primary biological cause – an imbalance of brain chemistry that can only be rectified by antipsychotic drugs. This pernicious assumption, rife within Western psychiatric systems, led to several important facts being ignored that might have had a major influence on the services offered to Millie. Life experiences, particularly traumatic ones, are a potent contributor to the development of psychosis. Antipsychotic medication is ineffective in one-in-three cases of psychosis, and a similar proportion can recover without drug treatment (see Chapter 8, pp. 152–4, for a review). Furthermore, there is evidence to suggest that the effectiveness of antipsychotic medication mainly derives from its generalised, arousal-reduction effect, and any return of psychotic symptoms upon withdrawal of the drug is as likely to represent a consequence of drug withdrawal (or discontinuation effect) as it is a 'relapse of the illness' (see Chapter 8, pp. 154–5). And as for low self-esteem: not only is it a powerful risk factor for the emergence of mental health problems; a negative self-view is also likely to hamper a person's recovery.

remain safe, avoid emotion

I could not figure out why Mark had made no progress in reducing his social anxiety. It was only during our tenth session of psychological therapy that the fundamental obstruction was revealed.

At the age of 42, he had been referred to our community mental health team by his GP, after Mark had described suffering long-standing anxieties about interacting with people, typically experiencing heart palpitations, excessive sweating and a sense of imminent humiliation. Although his current difficulty with social anxiety would normally have been viewed by services as a 'mild to moderate' problem and therefore suitable for treatment within the primary care setting (involving sessions with a psychological therapist at his local GP practice), Mark was referred to our psychiatric team because 20 years ago he had been diagnosed with paranoid schizophrenia and was therefore deemed to have a 'severe mental illness'. Despite the absence of psychotic symptoms for almost two decades, Mark was adjudged to require the higher-intensity input of a multidisciplinary team, including psychiatrists, to manage his anxiety problem.

During my initial therapy sessions with Mark I learned that he was homosexual and had, for the most part, kept his sexual orientation a secret from his family and friends. A pervasive sense of being different from other people typified his youth, and while completing his accountancy degree at university he often felt 'alienated' from his student peers. Nevertheless, he studied hard and achieved a first-class honours degree which earned a job at a prestigious accountancy firm in London. Unfortunately, six months after moving to the capital, he was the victim of a violent assault in his own home. Intruders broke into his flat in the early hours of the morning, believing there to be a vast amount of money hidden away, and beat Mark about the head and body with baseball bats, demanding that he tell them where the cash was concealed. Unsurprisingly, after this traumatic experience Mark became increasingly distrustful of people, suffered insomnia and drank heavily in an attempt to cope with his anxieties. His problems escalated and, at 22 years of age, he experienced a severe and prolonged episode of paranoia (being convinced that he was about to be murdered by an elite group of paratroopers from Russia) that necessitated a six-month admission to a psychiatric inpatient ward. It was at this point he acquired the schizophrenia tag.

While in hospital he had been prescribed a range of antipsychotic drugs. At the point at which his paranoia subsided, he had been taking olanzapine and he had continued to take this drug for the subsequent 20 years. Following discharge from hospital, Mark had gradually returned to the accountancy world, while keeping secret both his sexuality and mental health history from his employers and work colleagues.

By the time he presented to our community mental health team, Mark was a rare example of someone with a diagnosis of schizophrenia continuing to hold down a responsible, highly paid job. As a senior accountant for a brewing company, he managed four junior accountants and was ultimately responsible for overseeing the firm's tax liabilities and annual accounts. He performed these duties well and had recently been promoted. Away from work, however, Mark's life was impoverished. He lived alone and had no friends outside of the work environment. For the most part, he could communicate effectively with colleagues at his accountancy firm – 'I can put on a front at work' – but interactions with people outside of the work environment evoked high levels of anxiety and he actively avoided such encounters. He declined all invitations to socialise with his work colleagues. Outside of office hours his life adhered to a rigid structure, with set times for shopping, weekly visits to his elderly father and a trip to the pharmacy to pick up his tablets. In addition to prescribed medication, he smoked cannabis on a daily basis (three joints each evening and one in the morning before going to work) and purchased Valium off the Internet, which he used intermittently in anticipation of difficult meetings at his accountancy firm.

I had at first been optimistic Mark would make some quick gains from psychological therapy. He understood how his avoidance of social situations impeded progress. He recognised how his use of cannabis and Valium was counterproductive and he expressed genuine intentions to make changes. He also quickly grasped how his negative predictions about social encounters (for example, 'I'll make a total idiot of myself') served to heighten his anxieties, and he could recognise the benefits of challenging these thoughts by means of the therapy. Despite all these insights, and his hard work at implementing what he had learned in therapy, by our tenth session Mark had made very little progress.

The fundamental barrier to progress was identified when we explored a recent instance where, after committing himself to attending a small social gathering to commemorate his father's birthday, he opted out.

'At what point did you decide that you were not going to attend?' I asked.

'Just before I was about to set off,' Mark said. 'I rang my father and lied that I had a chest infection and didn't want to risk passing it on to him.'

'At the moment just prior to you deciding that you were not going to go to the party, how were you feeling?' I asked.

'Very anxious and panicky.'

'What specific thoughts were running through your mind at the moment you were feeling panicky?'

'As always I was anticipating I would make a fool of myself, show myself up in front of them all. I knew my brother-in-law would be there, spouting his usual Tory claptrap about benefit scroungers and the like.'

Mark and I had spent a lot of therapy time challenging the validity of his prediction that he would make a fool of himself in front of people. For example, we had calculated that over the past 20 years he would have had this thought over 1,000 times and that on every occasion it had proven to be incorrect, Mark managing the social encounter without any such humiliation.

'In light of all the evidence we have generated against the "I'll make a fool of myself" belief, what do you think made it so plausible to you when you were about to leave for your father's birthday celebration?'

Mark's cheeks reddened and he avoided my gaze, instead looking at the floor. 'I still believe I will lose control and start acting crazy; talking nonsense like I did all those years ago,' said Mark, his eyes moistening.

'You mean you fear you will have another psychotic episode?'

'Yes,' said Mark, 'it would only take a moronic comment about all the welfare cheats in this country. I would argue with him and I would completely lose it and get sectioned again.'

'How do you make sense of the fact that that's never happened over the last 20 years?'

'Because I've managed to avoid feeling emotion. I avoid arguments, in case I get angry. I've opted out of ever finding a partner as I don't want to risk the turmoil of a break-up. And I've stopped watching football on television, or listening to my favourite music, in case the excitement triggers another episode of my illness.'

Mark's rigid and impoverished lifestyle, together with his daily dose of cannabis, now made more sense to me; he was continuously striving to evade any form of emotional arousal lest it should precipitate further psychotic experiences and confinement in a psychiatric hospital.

'How did you form this idea that feeling emotion would evoke further periods of illness?' I asked.

'Dr Crompton, the consultant psychiatrist in London, explained schizophrenia to me. He told me it was a brain defect that I had genetically inherited and that it could be activated by stressful life experiences. Once I had recovered, he said I must continue taking my olanzapine, and try to avoid any stress in the future, or my schizophrenia would return.'

So Mark had spent 20 years of his life believing himself to be the carrier of a brain deficit, a biological incendiary device in his head that would be detonated by a powerful emotional experience. Little wonder that he constantly felt on the cusp of something disastrous, and thereby lived a restricted, mundane existence.

The 'illness like any other' doctrine, as the vignettes illustrate, is the driving force behind many unhelpful practices within psychiatric services. Three specific assumptions, all without persuasive evidence to support them, underpin these practices:

1. The primary cause of mental health problems is a genetic brain disorder.
2. Once severe mental illness is diagnosed, direct intervention at the biological level (that is, medication or electro-convulsive therapy) is necessary.
3. There is a clear demarcation between the mentally ill and people not afflicted by mental illness.

Some psychiatric professionals (like Dr Crompton in his discussions with Mark) explicitly espouse these assumptions. Many more act in a way that implicitly endorses them.

witches of the twenty-first century

part I: the stigma of being a psychiatric patient

Forty years ago, Thomas Szasz (a forthright critic of psychiatry) asserted society's enduring need to scapegoat, by drawing parallels between the seventeenth-century witch-hunts and the modern treatment of those people identified as mentally ill (Szasz, 1973). Today, the stigma suffered by those experiencing mental health problems is often described as more disabling than the mental disorder itself. Paradoxically, the main promoter of this stigma is the very psychiatric system commissioned by the taxpayer to provide professional help for those suffering psychological distress.

After defining what is meant by stigma, the first part of this chapter will elucidate the array of negative consequences associated with being identified as a user of psychiatric services in Western society. The specific ways by which traditional psychiatric practices stigmatise its service users will then be described. The second part of the chapter will provide real examples of these stigmatising processes in action within our current psychiatric system.

what is stigma?

A succinct definition of stigma is: 'A sign of disgrace or discredit which sets a person apart from others' (Byrne, 2000, p. 65). Terminology can be confusing, however, with similar and overlapping concepts being used in the literature. For example, the term 'prejudice' has historically represented emotions of antipathy based on faulty information (Allport, 1954) and has featured in narratives relating to race, while stigma has been employed in the context of mental health problems. Nonetheless, a recent study has demonstrated that the terms have much in common (Phelan et al., 2008).

An important distinction has been drawn between public stigma (the reaction of the general population to people with mental health problems) and self-stigma (the prejudice that those afflicted with such disorders turn upon themselves) (Corrigan & Watson, 2002). With regards to self-stigma, there is substantial evidence to suggest that people who are aware of social stereotypes start to concur and apply them to their own self-concept (Corrigan, Rafacz & Rusch, 2011), a pernicious process that might account for the poor self-esteem and low confidence characteristic of psychiatric service users.

Social scientists have elaborated the stigma concept and identified the psychological and social processes involved. Goffman (1963) proposed two requirements for someone to be stigmatised. Firstly, a distinguishing sign which may be either visible (such as gender or skin colour) or invisible (such as a mental health problem). According to Goffman, if the sign is observable the person is 'discredited' whereas if it is invisible the person is 'discreditable'. Secondly, the sign has to be associated with a negative attribution. Combination of these two components results in the individual becoming disqualified from full membership of society.

Drawing on some aspects of Goffman's ideas, Link and Phelan (2001) developed what has arguably been the most influential model of stigma. Although subsequently elaborated, the initial formulation of their social-cognitive model proposed four elements: labelling, stereotyping, separation and loss of status/discrimination.

Labelling functions to define and categorise, and has similarity to Goffman's 'sign', but emphasises that it is the observer who is doing the evaluating rather than it representing an inherent part of the person being stigmatised. Stereotyping is an automatic cognitive process by which a label becomes associated with a set of negative characteristics, thereby allowing rapid categorisation. Labelling and stereotyping can lead to separation, an 'us' and 'them' mentality, which in turn renders the out-group susceptible to both discrimination and a loss of status, the former being the active behavioural component that denies people access to opportunities and resources. The type of discrimination that occurs is related to the emotion associated with the attitude; for example, fear will evoke social distance (Corrigan, Kerr & Knudson, 2005).

the consequences of stigma

The evidence is unequivocal that stigma blights the experiences of people with mental health problems. The process may be insidious or manifest but, either way, for those people unfortunate enough to be identified as suffering from a mental disorder, it impairs functioning in the personal, social and vocational domains of their lives. Research involving in-depth discussions with people diagnosed as schizophrenic has demonstrated that stigma can cause more impairment than the mental disorder itself, thereby effectively being a 'second illness' (Schulze & Angermeyer, 2003).

The specific consequences of stigma for people suffering mental health problems are summarised below.

the psychosis stereotype

Stereotyping allows for rapid decisions to be made about a group of people and requires minimal effort of thought, thus preserving cognitive functions for other tasks (Fiske, 1993; Hamilton & Sherman, 1994; Crandall, 2000). With regards to judgements about people with mental health problems, these snap decisions are likely to occur in a context of low knowledge, as research has consistently demonstrated that the public are mostly ignorant about psychiatric disorders and are prone to endorse many misunderstandings (Gaebel et al., 2002).

Despite those with a diagnosis of schizophrenia being 14 times more likely to be the victims of a violent crime than to commit one (Brekke et al., 2001), people who experience psychoses are typically perceived as dangerous, violent and unpredictable, the upshot being that the general public (across several countries of the developed world) have a desire to maintain social distance (Angermeyer & Matschinger, 1994, 2003; Crisp et al., 2000; Jorm & Wright, 2008). There is substantial evidence that the media is guilty of perpetuating these negative stereotypes about people with mental health problems. An analysis of over 3,000 American newspaper stories that made reference to someone with a psychiatric disorder found that 39 per cent of them focused on violence or dangerousness (Corrigan, Watson et al., 2005). A similar study by Coverdale, Nairn and Claasen (2002), analysing over 600 mental health news stories in New Zealand, reported that over 60 per cent portrayed this group of people as dangerous. These negative images of mental health are not restricted to newspapers; films and television are also culpable (Thornicroft, 2006).

secrecy and social distancing

The psychosis stereotype may be associated with sufferers tending towards secrecy about their difficulties and may partly explain why people with psychosis have smaller social networks (Howard, Leese & Thornicroft, 2000). A German study (Hillert et al., 1999) found that the public were much less likely to talk about their mental disorders to friends and relatives than they were to talk about physical disorders. With regards to depression, it has long been known that the majority of people in the United Kingdom would be embarrassed to discuss this ubiquitous disorder with their general practitioner for fear of being viewed as imbalanced or neurotic (Priest et al., 1996).

Recently, a comprehensive study of discrimination, involving 700 people with psychosis across 27 countries, revealed that 72 per cent felt the need to conceal their diagnosis and almost half struggled to make and keep friends (Thornicroft et al., 2009).

harassment and abuse
According to studies commissioned by the mental health charity Mind, not all consequences of stigma are covert – negative attitudes towards those with mental health problems often being blatant and crude. A questionnaire survey of people with mental health problems by Read and Baker (1996) found that 47 per cent of respondents said they had been verbally abused in public, 14 per cent had been physically assaulted and 26 per cent had been forced to move home, owing to harassment. A more recent study (Mind, 2007) suggested that such victimisation was becoming more commonplace. Over the two-year period prior to the survey, 71 per cent reported victimisation, including 22 per cent who had been physically assaulted.

Although these surveys are unable to distinguish the proportion of harassment that is attributable to the mental health problem per se, rather than a general consequence of disproportionately living in less affluent neighbourhoods characterised by higher crime rates, the respondents typically believed that the victimisation was related to their mental health histories.

loss of valued roles
According to the Read and Baker (1996) survey, employment opportunities for people with mental health problems are less than for those with physical problems. Interestingly, 69 per cent had been put off applying for jobs, suggestive of self-stigma fuelling the anticipation of rejection. Furthermore, 34 per cent believed they had been dismissed from a job as a direct result of their mental disorders. An earlier study (Regier et al., 1988) found that Americans were reticent about disclosing depression, fearing it would have a negative impact upon employment opportunities. The international study by Thornicroft et al. (2009)

concluded that 29 per cent of people diagnosed with schizophrenia experienced negative discrimination in relation to both finding and keeping a job. Additional injustices may operate when applying for loans or insurance (Read & Baker, 1996).

More alarmingly, the experience of suffering mental health problems may elicit negative attitudes from others about the prospect of parenthood. The Read and Baker (1996) study not only reported that 38 per cent of psychiatric patients in a parental role believed that their ability to look after children had been unfairly questioned, but also includes an anecdote of a 33-year-old psychosis sufferer whose husband was told by the consultant psychiatrist not to have children as they would inevitably be taken away.

In conclusion, a person identified with a mental health problem is confronted with an array of discriminatory practices, and warped reporting by the media unhelpfully reinforces the public's negative attitudes. Nevertheless, the most pernicious generator of stigma is located much closer to the psychiatric home.

how traditional psychiatry promotes stigma

It is a supreme paradox that the most potent source of stigma for people with mental health problems is the network of established clinical and research practices of psychiatric professionals. Although enthusiasts of biological ('illness like any other') models of mental disorder are most culpable, all professionals employed within the psychiatric system inadvertently contribute, to some degree, to the stigmatisation of the very people they are paid to help.

Traditional psychiatry inflicts stigma on its service users in three main ways, namely, via: the promotion of biogenetic explanations of mental disorders; the attitude and behaviour of professional staff; and the use of diagnostic labels. Each of these will now be discussed in more detail.

stigmatisation through biogenetic explanations

The beliefs people hold about the primary causes of mental disorders will influence attitudes towards those exhibiting these problems. Essentialist beliefs that social categories are fixed and intrinsic are implicated in the development of a range of society's prejudices, anti-gay bigotry being one example (Haslam, Rothschild & Ernst, 2002). In a similar way, the stubborn insistence of biological psychiatry that psychotic and depressive problems are primarily caused by genetically inherited brain abnormalities (see Chapter 2, pp. 18–9) can lead to a negative view of the mentally ill (Mehta & Farina, 1997). A recent review of the relevant literature by Read et al. (2006) found that, in 11 out of 12 studies, biogenetic explanations were associated with more negative attitudes as compared to explanations based on a person's life experiences.

More specifically, a belief about biogenetic causation of mental health problems has been shown: to be associated with a reluctance to befriend or enter into romantic involvement with people experiencing these problems (Golding et al., 1975; Read & Harre, 2001); to view them as a childlike non-person (Sarbin & Mancuso, 1970); and to enhance perceptions of dangerousness and unpredictability (Read & Harre, 2001; Walker & Read, 2002).

Furthermore, the Mehta and Farina (1997) study suggested that people holding biogenetic views of causation are predisposed to behave in a harsher way towards those deemed to have a mental health problem. Fifty-five male students participated in a learning test that explored their behaviour towards a partner who they understood to have a history of mental health problems. When the partners' difficulties were described in disease terms, the respondents increased the electric shocks quicker as compared to when they were presented with psychosocial explanations attributing the mental health problems to childhood experiences.

Despite the substantial body of evidence demonstrating that biogenetic explanations of mental disorders promote and maintain stigma towards sufferers, traditional psychiatry has attempted to 'educate' the public that psychoses are biochemical brain diseases (for a review, see Read and Haslam, 2004). Both American (Wahl, 1987, 1999) and Australian (Jorm, Angermeyer & Katschnig, 2000; Jorm et al., 1997) anti-stigma researchers have strived to promote what has been termed 'mental health literacy'. The concept of health literacy originally emerged in relation to physical health and was intended to encourage people to access and understand relevant information so as to promote and maintain better health (Nutbeam et al. 1993). A logical and helpful application of this concept to mental health would have involved a focus on wellbeing, early intervention initiatives and the development of psychologically healthy systems in the home, the work environment and in our general communities. Instead, advocates of biological psychiatry have promoted spurious biogenetic models of mental disorder which, if accepted, would negatively impact on people with mental health problems. These educational initiatives, often enthusiastically supported by the pharmaceutical industry, have proceeded despite a body of evidence indicating that life experiences are much more potent predictors of mental health problems than genes or brain abnormalities (see Chapter 2, pp. 24–6).

Ironically, the general public hold a more enlightened view of the causes of mental disorder than biological psychiatrists. When asked for their views as to what might cause a person to experience the signs of depression or psychosis they typically propose psychosocial contributors such as environmental stress, bereavement or trauma (Read & Haslam, 2004).

stigmatisation through the behaviour of mental health professionals

Research conducted with the users of psychiatric services has indicated that they encounter worse attitudes from health professionals than they do from the general public. Surveys and interviews with mental health service users and their families suggested that professionals within the psychiatric system were a more potent source of stigma and discrimination than any other sector of society and, as such, are the group most in need of reform (Walter, 1998; Pinfold et al., 2005). Qualitative research by González-Torres et al. (2007) highlighted that service users diagnosed with schizophrenia often felt they were not believed by professionals and that their physical problems were underestimated – a disturbing finding given the potentially serious side effects of taking antipsychotic medication.

All mental health professionals collude with practices that discriminate against people with mental disorders. The most fundamental example concerns the implementation of the Mental Health Act (1983, 2007), the central piece of legislation in England and Wales that allows those deemed to suffer from a mental illness to be detained against their will in hospital, irrespective of whether they have committed a crime (see Chapter 4, pp. 62–5, for further discussion). More subtle stigmatising practices include the pervasive perks (higher salary, more holidays, better pension entitlements) that have been awarded to mental health professionals (but not their counterparts in the physical health field) thereby implying that there is something more difficult or risky about working with the mentally ill. A further sign of the disadvantage faced by people with mental health problems is the rarity of ballot boxes in psychiatric hospitals, even in countries where they give high priority to human rights (Sartorius, 2002).

Some commentators have proposed that the stigmatisation of those with mental disorders may have a socio-regulatory function, psychiatric professionals being deployed by society to legitimise the exclusion of those deemed to be troublesome (Summerfield, 2001). Psychiatrists in particular have been willing collaborators in this process by encroaching into territory that has traditionally been reserved for lawyers and priests, thereby conflating medical and psychological facts with social values and expectations.

stigmatisation through diagnostic labelling

Although some service users find it reassuring to have their distress formally recognised with an explicit diagnosis, there is evidence that the application of labels to mental health problems can be stigmatising (Sartorius, 2002). Being labelled as suffering with a specific mental illness is associated with the perception of increased seriousness of a person's difficulties (Cormack & Furnham, 1998), more pessimism about the prospect of recovery (Angermeyer & Matschinger, 1996), greater likelihood of rejection (Sarbin & Mancuso, 1970) and the underestimation of a person's social skills (Read & Haslam, 2004).

The 'schizophrenic' label seems to be particularly pernicious. For example, a survey of over 5,000 German citizens found that the label 'schizophrenia' resulted in an inflated estimation of dangerousness and a greater likelihood of social exclusion (Angermeyer & Matschinger, 2003).

Despite a body of evidence concluding that psychiatric diagnoses are virtually meaningless (see Bentall, 2009, for a review), diagnostic classification systems are routinely referred to within psychiatric services throughout the Western world. One such system, the *Diagnostic and Statistical Manual* (American Psychiatric Association, 2013) was recently updated, the fifth edition incorporating 15 more mental disorders than its predecessor. Diagnostic classification systems such as this are often purported to be the clinicians' bible to enable communication about mental disorders. However, in addition to spuriously implying that each listed mental illness is primarily the product of a discrete biological aberration – 'an illness like any other' (see Chapter 2) – such high-profile labelling of mental health problems can only act to exacerbate the stigma experienced by users of psychiatric services.

how can we reduce stigma?

In recognition of its importance, a recent government policy document, *No Health Without Mental Health*, identified a reduction in stigma as one of the six priorities for healthcare in the United Kingdom (Department of Health, 2011). But how can such a shift in attitudes towards people with mental health problems be achieved?

Educational initiatives that give due emphasis to the psychosocial factors that contribute to the development and maintenance of mental disorders would be one effective approach to tackling stigma within society. As already documented, teaching spurious biogenetic models of mental illness exacerbates the social exclusion and prejudice that people with mental health problems suffer in their day-to-day lives. Conversely, informing the general public about how life experiences play a powerful role in the development of psychotic experiences and depression would be expected to promote more compassionate attitudes.

There is evidence to suggest that promoting psychosocial explanations of mental health problems can positively influence people's attitudes towards those afflicted. For example, four lectures to university students, highlighting how life experiences can lead to the emergence of severe psychiatric disorders, achieved improvements in attitudes, particularly around dangerousness and unpredictability (Read & Law, 1999). Similarly, Campbell et al. (2011) demonstrated how the teaching of psychosocial approaches to psychosis can reduce fear and the perceived need for social distance.

So one effective way of reducing stigma towards people with mental health problems is to deliver public education initiatives that provide a balanced view of the research literature on the causes of mental disorder to tell the general population the way it is rather than the way biological psychiatrists and drug companies would like it to be.

However, the most useful approach to eliminating stigma involves more than lecturing the public; it also includes the encouragement of direct contact between people suffering mental health problems and those who do not. Read and Harre (2001) found that those who reported greater contact with mentally ill people tended to have more positive attitudes towards them. Furthermore, anti-stigma campaigns that have achieved some beneficial effects have all involved direct contact with the users of psychiatric services (Corrigan et al., 2002; Couture & Penn, 2003; Schulze et al., 2003; Pinfold, Toulmin et al., 2003; Pinfold, Thornicroft et al., 2005; Chan, Mak & Law, 2009). The service users involved in these anti-stigma initiatives would also be expected to benefit from the experience, feeling a sense of empowerment that is likely to aid recovery (Pinfold, Toulmin et al., 2003).

The Schulze et al. (2003) study involved a straightforward approach that could easily be deployed more widely. As part of a programme of

German destigmatisation, the intervention involved a young person with a diagnosis of schizophrenia introducing himself to a group of secondary-school students and discussing his experiences, relevant treatments and the associated stigma. Improvements were recorded at one-month follow-up with regards to both student attitudes and their inclination to engage in social relationships with people identified as suffering with schizophrenia.

A similar study in the United Kingdom by Pinfold, Toulmin et al. (2003), involving both education and direct contact with users of mental health services, incorporated almost 500 schoolchildren, and found a small but significant increase in positive attitudes at both one-month and six-month follow-up. Larger studies in Canada and the United Kingdom, adopting the education and direct-contact approach, demonstrated a positive impact on desire for social distance (Pinfold, Thornicroft et al., 2005).

A Chinese project by Chan et al. (2009) used video presentations rather than 'live' service users, and also investigated whether the order of delivery of education and contact had any effect on outcomes. Positive results were reported with regards to both stigmatising attitudes and desire for social distance, with the education followed by direct (video) contact having the greater and more lasting effects.

In conclusion, challenging the stigma that blights the lives of many people with mental health problems is most effectively achieved by a combination of education, which gives due prominence to psychosocial factors, along with interactions with those who have experienced these mental disorders. The old adage 'seeing is believing' seems applicable here, where personal experience that is inconsistent with prevailing stereotypes is a transformer of attitudes.

references

Allport, G.W. (1954). *The Nature of Prejudice*. Reading, MA: Addison-Wesley.

American Psychiatric Association. (2013). *The Diagnostic and Statistical Manual of Mental Disorders* (5th ed.). Arlington, VA: American Psychiatric Association.

Angermeyer, M. & Matschinger, H. (1994). Lay beliefs about schizophrenic disorder: The results of a population study in Germany. *Acta Psychiatrica Scandinavia, 89*, 39.

Angermeyer, M. & Matschinger, H. (1996). The effects of labelling on the lay theory regarding schizophrenic disorders. *Social Psychiatry and Psychiatric Epidemiology, 31*, 316–20.

Angermeyer, M. & Matschinger, H. (2003). The stigma of mental illness: Effects of labelling on public attitudes toward people with mental disorder. *Acta Psychiatrica Scandinavia, 108*(4), 304–9.

Bentall, R.P. (2009). *Doctoring the Mind: Why psychiatric treatments fail.* London: Penguin Books.

Brekke, J.S., Prindle, C., Bae, S.W. & Long, J.D. (2001). Risks for individuals with schizophrenia who are living in the community. *Psychiatric Services, 52*, 1358–66.

Byrne, P. (2000). Stigma of mental illness and ways of diminishing it. *Advances in Psychiatric Treatment, 6*, 65–2.

Campbell, M., Shryane, N., Byrne, R. & Morrison, A.P. (2011). A mental health promotion approach to reducing discrimination about psychosis in teenagers. *Psychosis: Psychological, Social and Integrative Approaches, 3*(1), 41–51.

Chan, J.Y.N., Mak, W.W.S. & Law, L.S.C. (2009). Combining education and video-based contact to reduce stigma of mental illness: 'The Same or Not the Same' anti-stigma program for secondary schools in Hong Kong. *Social Science & Medicine, 68*(8), 1521–6.

Cormack, S. & Furnham, A. (1998). Psychiatric labelling, sex role stereotypes and beliefs about the mentally ill. *International Journal of Social Psychiatry, 44*, 235–47.

Corrigan, P.W., Kerr, A. & Knudsen, L. (2005). The stigma of mental illness: Explanatory models and methods for change. *Applied and Preventive Psychology, 11*(3), 179–90.

Corrigan, P.W., Rafacz, J. & Rusch, N. (2011). Examining a progressive model of self-stigma and its impact on people with serious mental illness. *Psychiatry Research, 189*(3), 339–43.

Corrigan, P.W., Rowan, D., Green, A., Lundin, R., River, P., Uphoff-Wasowski, K. et al. (2002). Challenging two mental illness stigmas: Personal responsibility and dangerousness. *Schizophrenia Bulletin, 28*, 293–309.

Corrigan, P.W. & Watson, A.C. (2002). The paradox of self-stigma and mental illness. *Clinical Psychology: Science and Practice, 9*(1), 35–53.

Corrigan, P.W., Watson, A.C., Gracia, G., Slopen, N., Rasinki, K. & Hall, L.L. (2005). Newspaper stories as measures of structural stigma. *Psychiatric Services, 56*(5), 551–6.

Couture, S. & Penn, D. (2003). Interpersonal contact and the stigma of mental illness: A review of the literature. *Journal of Mental Health, 12*(3), 291–305.

Coverdale, J., Nairn, R. & Claasen, D. (2002). Depictions of mental illness in print media: A prospective national sample. *Australian and New Zealand Journal of Psychiatry, 36*(5), 697–700.

Crandall, C.S. (2000). Ideology and lay theories of stigma: The justification of stigmatization. In T.F. Heatherton, R.E. Kleck, M.R. Hebl & J.G. Hull (Eds.), *The Social Psychology of Stigma* (pp. 126–50). New York: Guilford Press.

Crisp, A.H., Gelder, M.G., Rix, S., Meltzer, H.I. & Rolands, O.J. (2000). Stigmatisation of people with mental illnesses. *British Journal of Psychiatry*, *177*, 4–7.

Department of Health. (2011). *No Health Without Mental Health: A cross-government mental health outcomes strategy for people of all ages.* London: Central Office of Information.

Fiske, S. (1993). Controlling other people: The impact of power on stereotyping. *American Psychologist*, *48*, 621–43.

Gaebel, W., Baumann, A., Witte, A.M. & Zaeske, H. (2002). Public attitudes towards people with mental illness in six German cities. *European Archives of Psychiatry and Clinical Neuroscience*, *252*, 278–87.

Goffman, E. (1963). *Stigma: Notes on the management of spoiled identity.* Englewood Cliffs, NJ: Prentice-Hall.

Golding, S.L., Becker, E., Sherman, S. & Rappaport, J. (1975). The Behavioral Expectations Scale: Assessment of expectations for interaction with the mentally ill. *Journal of Consulting and Clinical Psychology*, *43*, 109.

González-Torres, M., Oraa, R., Aristegui, M., Fernández-Rivas, A. & Guimon, J. (2007). Stigma and discrimination towards people with schizophrenia and their family members. *Social Psychiatry and Psychiatric Epidemiology*, *42*(1), 14–23.

Hamilton, D.L. & Sherman, J.W. (1994). Stereotypes. In R.S. Wyer & T.K. Srull (Eds.), *Handbook of Social Cognition* (Vol. 2; pp. 1–68). Hillsdale, NJ: Erlbaum.

Haslam, N., Rothschild, L. & Ernst, D. (2002). Are essentialist beliefs associated with prejudice? *British Journal of Social Psychology*, *41*, 87–100.

Hillert, A., Sandmann, J., Ehmig, S.C., Weisbecker, H., Kepplinger, H.M., Benkert, O. et al. (1999). The general public's cognitive and emotional perception of mental illnesses: An alternative to attitude-research. In J. Guimon, W. Fischer & N. Sartorius (Eds.), *The Image of Madness: The public facing mental illness and psychiatric treatments* (pp. 56–71). Basel: Karger.

Howard, L., Leese, M. & Thornicroft, G. (2000). Social networks and functional status in patients with psychosis. *Acta Psychiatrica Scandinavica*, *102*(5), 376–85.

Jorm, A.F., Angermeyer, M. & Katschnig, H. (2000). Public knowledge of and attitudes to mental disorders. In G. Andrews & S. Henderson (Eds.), *Unmet Need in Psychiatry* (pp. 399–413). Cambridge: Cambridge University Press.

Jorm, A.F., Korten, A.E., Jacomb, P.A., Christensen, H., Rodgers, D. & Pollitt, P. (1997). Public beliefs about causes and risk factors for depression and schizophrenia. *Social Psychiatry and Psychiatric Epidemiology*, *32*, 143–8.

Jorm, A.F. & Wright, A. (2008). Influences upon young people's stigmatising attitudes towards peers with mental disorders: National survey of young Australians and their parents. *The British Journal of Psychiatry*, *192*(2), 144–9.

Link, B.G. & Phelan, J.C. (2001). Conceptualizing stigma. *Annual Review of Sociology*, *27*(1), 363–85.

Mehta, S. & Farina, A. (1997). Is being 'sick' really better? Effect of the disease view of mental disorder on stigma. *Journal of Social and Clinical Psychology*, *16*, 405–19.

Mental Health Act. (1983). Retrieved 21 April 2014 from http://www.legislation.gov.uk/ukpga/1983/20/contents

Mental Health Act. (2007). Retrieved 14 April 2013 from http://www.legislation.gov.uk/ukpga/2007/12/contents

Mind. (2007). *Another Assault: Mind's campaign for equal access to justice for people with mental health problems.* London: Mind.

Nutbeam, D., Wise, M., Bauman, A., Harris, E. & Leeder, S. (1993). *Goals and Targets for Australia's Health in the Year 2000 and Beyond.* Canberra: AGPS.

Phelan, J.C., Link, B.G. & Dovidio, D.F. (2008). Stigma and prejudice: One animal or two? *Social Science Medicine*, *67*(3), 358–67.

Pinfold, V., Thornicroft, G., Huxley, P. & Farmer, P. (2005). Active ingredients in anti-stigma programmes in mental health. *International Review of Psychiatry*, *17*(2), 123–31.

Pinfold, V., Toulmin, H., Thornicroft, G., Huxley, P., Farmer, P. & Graham, T. (2003). Reducing psychiatric stigma and discrimination: Evaluation of educational interventions in UK secondary schools. *British Journal of Psychiatry*, *182*, 342–6.

Priest, R.G., Vize, C., Roberts, A., Roberts, M. & Tylee, A. (1996). Lay people's attitudes to treatment of depression: Results of opinion poll for Defeat Depression campaign just before its launch. *British Medical Journal*, *313*, 858–9.

Read, J. & Baker, S. (1996). *Not Just Sticks and Stones: A survey of the stigma, taboos and discrimination experienced by people with mental health problems.* London: Mind.

Read, J. & Harre, N. (2001). The role of biological and genetic causal beliefs in the stigmatisation of 'mental patients'. *Journal of Mental Health*, *10*, 223–35.

Read, J. & Haslam, N. (2004). Public opinion: Bad things happen and can drive you crazy. In J. Read, L.R. Mosher & R.P. Bentall (Eds.), *Models of Madness: Psychological, social and biological approaches to schizophrenia* (pp. 133–45). London: Routledge.

Read, J., Haslam, N., Sayce, L. & Davies, E. (2006). Prejudice and schizophrenia: A review of the 'mental illness is an illness like any other' approach. *Acta Psychiatrica Scandinavica, 114*(5), 303–18.

Read, J. & Law, A. (1999). The relationship of causal beliefs and contact with users of mental health services to attitudes to the 'mentally ill'. *International Journal of Psychiatry, 45*, 216–29.

Regier, D., Boyd, J., Burke, J., Rae, D., Myers, J., Kramer, M. et al. (1988). One-month prevalence of mental disorders in the United States. *Archives of General Psychiatry, 45*, 977–86.

Sarbin, T. & Mancuso, J. (1970). Failure of a moral enterprise: Attitude of the public toward mental illness. *Journal of Consulting and Clinical Psychology, 35*, 159–73.

Sartorius, N. (2002). Iatrogenic stigma of mental illness: Begins with behaviour and attitudes of medical professionals, especially psychiatrists. *British Medical Journal, 324*, 1470–1.

Schulze, B. & Angermeyer, M. (2003). Subjective experiences of stigma: A focus group study of schizophrenic patients, their relatives and mental health professionals. *Social Sciences and Medicine, 56*(2), 299–312.

Schulze, B., Richter-Werling, M., Matschinger, H. & Angermeyer, M.C. (2003). Crazy? So what! Effects of a school project on students' attitudes towards people with schizophrenia. *Acta Psychiatrica Scandinavica, 107*, 142–50.

Summerfield, D. (2001). Does psychiatry stigmatize? *Journal of the Royal Society of Medicine, 94*, 148–9.

Szasz, T.S. (1973). *The Manufacture of Madness: A comparative study of the Inquisition and the mental health movement.* London: Routledge & Keegan Paul.

Thornicroft, G. (2006). *Shunned: Discrimination against people with mental illness.* New York: Oxford University Press.

Thornicroft, G., Brohan, E., Rose, D., Sartorius, N. & Leese, M. (2009). Global pattern of experienced and anticipated discrimination against people with schizophrenia: A cross-sectional survey. *The Lancet, 373*(9661), 408–15.

Wahl, O. (1987). Public vs professional conceptions of schizophrenia. *Journal of Community Psychology, 15*, 285–91.

Wahl, O. (1999). Mental health consumers' experience of stigma. *Schizophrenia Bulletin, 25*, 467–78.

Walker, I. & Read, J. (2002). The differential effectiveness of psychosocial and biogenetic causal explanations in reducing negative attitudes towards 'mental illness'. *Psychiatry*, *65*, 313–25.

Walter, G. (1998). The attitude of health professionals towards carers and individuals with mental illness. *Australian Psychiatry*, *6*, 70–2.

part II: discrimination in action

staff and patients learning together? how absurd!

It was the last Thursday of November 2012 and around 20 members of the community mental health team had gathered for their monthly business meeting. Seated along the edges of the meeting room were psychiatric nurses, social workers, community care workers, an occupational therapist, a psychiatrist, a psychologist and a couple of managers. The agenda was long and the subsequent discussions were, for the most part, rather dull: how the team is failing to document the marital status of patients; the routine for opening and closing the building in light of the caretaker's long-term sickness; and a request to all team members not to leave their dirty cups and plates in the kitchen sink.

Towards the end of the meeting, in response to the 'Any other business' item, Helen (the team psychologist) raised her hand.

'Could I say a bit about a new group I would like to run here?'

Gill, the team manager and chairperson, nodded for her to proceed.

'I would like to facilitate a weekly "Mindfulness" group,' said Helen. 'For those who might not be familiar with the concept, mindfulness is a skill that involves bringing our full attention and awareness to the present moment, rather than our minds ruminating about the past or worrying about the future.'

There were some murmurs of approval in the room. Despite the dominant treatment approach within the community mental health service being medication, several professionals within the team were genuinely interested in extending the range of psychosocial (non-medical) interventions available to the service users.

'It sounds good to me,' said Gill.

'Could you tell us the kind of problems the group is best suited for?' asked one of the psychiatric nurses. 'So that we know which patients to refer in to the group.'

'Mindfulness is a very versatile skill that can potentially be useful for a wide range of mental health problems,' said Helen. 'So anyone who feels generally stressed might benefit. More specifically, the research has shown that mindfulness can be effective for managing depression and the range of anxiety problems.'

More members of the team expressed interest in the group. A couple of psychiatric nurses, who were both recognised as being wedded to biological treatments for mental illness, appeared disinterested, one yawning and the other glancing at her watch; after all, it was nearly lunch time.

The senior manager in attendance, Chris, had only just re-joined the meeting after leaving the room to take a phone call. 'It is very encouraging to hear that we are improving access to these talking therapies,' he said. 'As an organisation we are tasked with making these alternative treatments available to more patients.'

'There is one other thing,' said Helen. 'I'd like to open the group to staff as well as service users.'

A shroud of silence fell upon the meeting. The only sound was that of rain splattering on the window panes. Most of those present sat, heads bowed. The two bored nurses glanced at each other, puzzlement etched on their faces.

Sensing the unease in the room, Helen broke the hush. 'We all have stressful jobs – the clinicians and the secretarial staff. Learning mindfulness skills could benefit us all.'

Some people fidgeted. Eye contact was avoided, with some professional colleagues gazing into space while others seemed to become curious about the fine detail of their hands and fingernails.

Gill sought clarification. 'I assume you mean having some groups for staff and others for patients, perhaps alternating each week from one group to the other?'

'No,' said Helen, 'my intention would be to open the group to everyone so that we would have mixed groups of staff and service users, learning mindfulness side by side.'

The two bored nurses were now smirking at each other and rolling their eyes. Sporadic mutterings could be heard in the room, insufficiently loud to identify words. It was Chris who articulated what many team members were thinking. 'That's not going to happen,' he said with the commanding tone of a senior manager, 'as it would be entirely inappropriate.'

Encouraged by this authoritative endorsement, other team colleagues proffered their views.

'I'm not going to let the patients know about my stress levels; that would be unprofessional,' said a nurse.

'I wouldn't be able to relax if there were patients in the group,' said a social worker.

'I might slip up and disclose something about my personal life,' said one of the bored nurses, 'and the patients might use it against me.'

'But we're talking about a mindfulness group that involves the learning of a discrete skill; it's not analytical psychotherapy where we're expected to discuss our most intimate childhood experiences,' said Helen, her voice betraying her growing sense of exasperation.

'No, I cannot sanction a mixed group,' said Chris. 'It was only a few months ago that we had a violent assault on a member of staff in one of the other community teams; we are in the process of tightening up on the security of the building, so we would struggle to manage such a forum.'

And that closed down any further discussion of the issue.

The fact that managers and the majority of clinicians, within a specialist mental health team in the year 2012, were unwilling to sit alongside service users and learn a new skill demonstrates the expanse that psychiatric professionals have yet to travel to free themselves from stigmatising 'us and them' attitudes.

schizophrenia renders a person unfit to look after animals?

Barry had been in receipt of psychiatric services for over 15 years, during which time he had acquired several psychiatric diagnoses, including emotionally unstable personality disorder (an enduring condition characterised by mood instability, relationship problems and deliberate self-harm) and paranoid schizophrenia (a psychotic disorder associated with extreme suspiciousness and a sense of persecution). His recent history had included high-profile threats to commit suicide, involving the expressed intention to leap from the fifth storey of a car park. As a consequence of these behaviours, Barry had been admitted to an acute inpatient psychiatric ward on more than 20 occasions.

As the psychologist in a community mental health team, I had first met Barry when he was 37 years old following a request from a psychiatrist in the aftermath of a hospital admission. Like many people with mental health problems, Barry had endured a difficult life. As an infant he had suffered repeated physical abuse from his father, and subsequently his behaviour in mainstream school had become difficult to manage, leading to his exclusion. He was compelled to attend a special school where he received little academic input, instead spending the bulk of school time on a neighbouring farm looking after the animals. In his teenage years Barry was the victim of sexual abuse from adult males who took advantage of his naïvety and low intellect.

Given his life experiences, it was no surprise to discover that Barry found it difficult to trust people and displayed a negative self-view. During his lengthy contact with psychiatric services Barry had been prescribed a cocktail of tablets, including both antidepressant and antipsychotic medications, without any sustained benefit. Similarly futile had been attempts to engage Barry in talking therapies – his inability to read and write, and difficulties with abstract thinking, presenting formidable challenges for these forms of psychological intervention.

My early contacts with Barry were spent trying to understand his problems and to develop a trusting relationship with him. Once rapport was established, we agreed to pursue a practical approach to his difficulties, trying to improve his self-esteem by encouraging engagement in worthwhile activities to promote a sense of achievement. Discussion about Barry's typical week revealed a lifestyle devoid of the kind of things that maintain a person's wellbeing. Relationships with his wife and three daughters were chaotic and riddled with conflict and acrimony. Despite being a qualified joiner, he had not worked for over 15 years. He typically spent his days watching television, the monotony punctuated only by disputes with family members, often triggered by Barry's attempts to 'sort out' his daughters' problems; his interventions were almost always viewed as unwelcome interference in their lives. The only positive relationships in Barry's life were with psychiatric professionals, and even these were sporadic, his challenging and erratic behaviour often evoking negative reactions from professional staff and tarring Barry with the label of a 'heart-sink' patient.

During one of my psychology sessions I tried to pursue the possible value of voluntary work in improving Barry's self-esteem.

'What sort of things are you good at, or enjoy doing,' I asked.

'I don't know,' replied Barry. 'I'm not much good at anything.'

'Has anything in your life ever given you a sense of a job well done?'

'Looking after animals,' said Barry. 'I've always felt close to animals, and I love my dogs; I can't understand how people can be so cruel to them.'

Barry had two Labrador retrievers of his own which he doted on. He had often said that you can trust animals to never let you down (unlike people). The two dogs he owned were walked, groomed and well-nourished.

'How would you feel about doing some voluntary work, looking after animals that have been badly treated by their owners?' I asked.

'I'd love to,' said Barry, 'but I've tried to do that kind of thing before. They won't have me because I'm a mental patient.'

I found it difficult to believe that a history of mental health problems would trigger a blanket exclusion from the opportunity to look after animals on a voluntary basis; surely, such Draconian prohibition could not exist in a twenty-first century Western democracy.

After further discussion, Barry consented to me making some enquiries to a local animal sanctuary to find out whether there were any opportunities for him to do some part-time voluntary work. I rang the sanctuary the next day.

'We are always keen for an extra pair of hands,' said the manager, 'as long as he is kind to our animals.'

'I can vouch for his caring approach to animals,' I said. 'He has looked after dogs throughout most of his life and has done so very well. He does, however, have a long history of mental health problems. Is that likely to be an obstacle?'

'No, not at all,' said the pleasant lady on the other end of the phone. 'As long as he can do the work, that's all that matters. Ask him to come along for an introductory chat to find out a bit more about the kind of stuff we do.'

I shared this encouraging initial response with Barry and he was keen to pursue this opportunity. As he was anxious about interacting with new people, I agreed to go along with him on his first visit to the animal sanctuary. The meeting went very well, the manager and other staff giving lots of positive feedback about Barry's enthusiasm to care for animals. We were given an application form to complete and return to them – a bit of routine administration they were obliged to insist on, they said, and one that Barry needn't worry about.

As Barry was illiterate, we used our next meeting to complete the form. I read out the questions, and Barry told me what to write. Under the section 'History of medical problems', he told me to document that he suffered from 'paranoid schizophrenia'. Despite my suggestions that there might be more valid and informative ways of describing his mental health problems, Barry insisted that I include this diagnosis as he was keen to be open and honest from the outset.

Four weeks after posting the form, Barry had not received a response from the animal sanctuary. I encouraged Barry to phone the manager he had met on his visit, and who he had liked, for an update. Barry later informed me that the telephone conversation went something like this:

Barry: I'm ringing to find out if I can do some voluntary work. It's Barry; I came to talk with you about helping you look after your animals.

Manager: Oh yes, I remember.

Barry: I completed a form and sent it in to you. When will I be able to start?

Manager: I'm really sorry, Barry, but I'm not going to be able to offer you any work here.

Barry: Why's that?

Manager: I sought some advice about your schizophrenia and it is clear that my staff and I don't have the necessary skills to be able to manage your condition. I'm really sorry.

It remains unclear to this day where the 'advice' came from. Maybe the manager had not sought advice but had based her decision on her own misguided ideas about schizophrenia. Either way, Barry, a man with a love of animals and all the requisite skills for looking after them, was denied the opportunity of working voluntarily with them solely because of a diagnostic label.

don't believe her; she's insane!

I realised the court case had not gone well the instant I saw that she was wearing a black dress. Emma was sitting in the waiting room at the health centre on the morning of our scheduled psychology appointment. As I approached her I observed that her eyes were bloodshot and there was fresh scarring on her forearms, thereby confirming my initial impression.

Emma had been meeting with me for psychological therapy, on and off, for over two years, an unusually lengthy period of contact due to her complexity and erratic attendance for sessions. She was 28 years old when she was first referred to me and had a five-year history of contact with psychiatric services, during which time she acquired the diagnosis of bipolar disorder (a severe mental disorder characterised by pronounced mood swings ranging from overactive euphoria to profound depression). Diagnostic labels are notoriously unreliable and, as is often the case, Emma's array of recurring symptoms (mood swings, deliberate self-harm, substance misuse, extreme anger and unusual beliefs) had, at various points, been tagged as major depression, emotionally unstable personality disorder and schizophrenia.

Between the ages of 6 and 15, Emma had been sexually abused by her stepbrother (20 years her senior), a man with a major alcohol problem who routinely would crawl into Emma's bedroom on his hands and knees, oinking like a pig, and rape her. Although she suspected that her mother and younger brother knew about the abuse, it had never been spoken about. When she disclosed the sexual abuse to me during our second meeting I asked whether she had ever reported the rapes to the police. She informed me that she had not done so owing to fears that it would further damage the already-fragile relationships she currently had with family members, and she was adamant she did not wish to prosecute her abuser now.

Emma at first identified her recurrent self-mutilation, guilt about the abuse and low self-esteem as the priority problems she wished to address in therapy. A part of this work involved the sharing of documented experiences of other sexual-abuse survivors, along with the normalisation of the common reactions to such traumatic experiences such as self-blame, guilt and deliberate self-harm. In addition, Emma occasionally suffered 'flashbacks' to the abuse where a reminder of her past trauma evoked a reliving of her ordeal as if it was happening right now. For example, she related a disturbing experience of being in a shop when the smell of a man's aftershave (the same aftershave that her stepbrother wore) triggered a flashback during which she was paralysed with fear and started to oink like a pig.

Despite these difficulties, Emma had completed a university degree and was intent on making a career in journalism. When not experiencing the extremes of emotion, she presented as a vivacious and articulate young woman. By her own admission, she was a bit 'quirky'. She believed in ghosts and extraterrestrial life forms. Furthermore, she liked to dress in colours that represented her prevalent mood, black when depressed and garish shades of pink and yellow when euphoric.

After six months of psychological therapy Emma had achieved some small, but significant, improvements regarding her levels of guilt and self-blame. Maybe as a result of these changes, at the beginning of one of our psychology sessions she announced that she had decided to go ahead and prosecute her abuser, her motivation being her desire 'to punish the bastard who has destroyed my life'. We discussed at length the inevitably prolonged and stressful process involved in retrospectively bringing an abuser to justice but, unperturbed, Emma was adamant she wished to proceed. Later the same day she bravely attended a local police station and made a formal complaint about her stepbrother, who had last abused her 15 years ago.

As anticipated, the legal process was convoluted and emotionally fraught. Unusually for historical abuse cases, the evidence against the stepbrother seemed unequivocal. Not only did Emma courageously provide detailed evidence of the repeated and dehumanising abuse she suffered, but her younger brother also made a statement to the police describing how he had been frequently raped during his childhood by the same man. Much to Emma's surprise, a third witness (a childhood friend who was now working as a dentist and living 200 miles away) also came forward and testified that she had been sexually assaulted by Emma's stepbrother on one occasion as a child when she had been on a sleepover at their home.

Astonishingly, the jury found the stepbrother not guilty of all charges.

Clad in her black dress, oscillating between fury and despair, Emma spewed out what had happened in court. The barrister for the Crown Prosecution Service (CPS) had told Emma, prior to the hearing, that he was very confident of a conviction; after all, three victims would be testifying against the alleged abuser. But he had failed to foresee the strategic shenanigans of the female defence barrister.

In the first instance the defence barrister claimed that the evidences of both the brother and childhood friend were inadmissible on the basis that Emma would have, at some point, discussed the sexual abuse allegations with them prior to the case. The judge agreed, and directed the jury to discount their statements. After this success, all the defence barrister had to do to achieve a 'not guilty' verdict was to undermine and discredit Emma's testimony.

I suspect that the challenge of persuading members of a jury that Emma's evidence was unreliable was not the most difficult task the defence barrister would face during her career in the legal profession. After all, Emma had a raft of mental disorders and surely such patients could not be believed. Prior to the court hearing, the judge had acquiesced to the defence barrister's request to access Emma's psychiatric notes. Sifting through the clinical record allowed her to selectively highlight snippets of information that convinced the jury that Emma was not telling the truth: Emma was afflicted with schizophrenia and bipolar disorder; Emma routinely engaged in the seemingly irrational act of self-mutilation; Emma sometimes abused alcohol and drugs; Emma believed in ghosts; and Emma was known to oink like a pig in public places. The likelihood that the trauma of repeated childhood sexual abuse was the primary cause of her behaviour and mental health problems was never explained to the jury.

4

the witch-finder generals

part I: psychiatry and the misuse of power

Ronald Laing, a dissident British psychiatrist, famously quipped, 'I am still more frightened by the fearless power in the eyes of my fellow psychiatrists than by the powerless fear in the eyes of their patients' (Laing, 1985, p. 16). Power, or the lack of it, is central to understanding the modus operandi of psychiatric services within the developed world, and there is a huge power differential between those deemed to have mental health problems and the professional staff employed to help them.

This chapter will examine the major contributors to the pronounced power imbalance between psychiatric professionals and service users, and will also describe how psychiatrists have often exploited their privileged positions of authority through a combination of inappropriate medicalisation of human distress together with spurious claims that they are uniquely equipped to provide clinical leadership of multidisciplinary mental health teams. The second section of the chapter will illustrate this misuse of power within the current psychiatric system through a number of authentic anecdotes.

legalised discrimination: the mental health act

Two hundred and forty years ago the government of the day passed the Madhouse Act (1774) that, for the first time, installed the medical doctor in the role of arbiter of the insane (see Chapter 1, p. 3). Following further piecemeal legislation through the nineteenth and early twentieth centuries, much of it delegating greater powers to medical professionals in the management of people with mental disorders, it was not until the 1959 Mental Health Act that the state effectively surrendered its role in determining who should be incarcerated in psychiatric institutions, thereby allowing psychiatrists freedom to govern this group of vulnerable people (Szmukler & Holloway, 2000; Moncrieff, 2003).

Although the next major piece of mental health legislation, the Mental Health Act (1983), introduced more safeguards to protect the interests of patients, by the beginning of the twenty-first century the government's mindset shifted towards an irrational preoccupation with public safety, culminating in revisions to the Mental Health Act legislation in 2007. The upshot is that England and Wales now have a Mental Health Act that both legalises discrimination against people with mental health problems and sponsors psychiatric professionals to guarantee its implementation.

Under the auspices of the Mental Health Act psychiatric professionals can admit patients to hospital without their consent (commonly referred to as being 'sectioned') and subsequently force treatment upon them. By permitting incarceration without trial and the forcible administration of drugs, people with mental health problems are denied certain civil liberties that are afforded to all other citizens. Furthermore, as highlighted by Szmukler (2010), the current legislation is not compliant with the United Nations Convention on the Rights of Persons with Disabilities (United Nations, 2006), which states that 'The existence of a disability shall in no case justify a deprivation of liberty' (Article 14).

It is a fundamental tenet of Western democracies that a person is assumed innocent, and therefore immune from involuntary incarceration, until it is established that he or she is guilty of a crime. The Mental Health Act's deviation from this principle derives from the underlying assumption that people with mental illness present an appreciable risk to others, thereby colluding with the psychosis–violence stereotype (see Chapter 3, p. 41). As starkly asserted by Vassilev and Pilgrim (2007), their vulnerability to detention without trial, and without having committed any offence, tars psychiatric patients with a similar status to suspected terrorists. As such, the terms 'mental health services' and 'Mental Health Act' are misnomers, as no health interest of the patient is being served, their primary foci being the control of the patient and protection of the public.

The perils of collusion between the state and medicine have long been recognised. Szasz (1973) drew the distinction between 'institutional psychiatry' (characterised by coercion and a primary desire to protect society) and 'contractual psychiatry' (characterised by cooperation and a primary desire to help the individual). According to Szasz, Mental Health Act legislation inevitably results in the views of psychiatrists acceding to those of the government of the day and to their acting as agents of the state. Szasz also drew parallels between the witch-hunts of medieval times and the way psychiatric patients are viewed today; given the inflated assumptions of dangerousness implicit within the Mental Health Act, it seems inevitable that those people tagged as suffering with mental health problems would become scapegoats for the ills endemic within society. Indeed, more recent commentators have endorsed these concerns, asserting that psychiatry acts to legitimise the exclusion of unwanted sections of the community (Summerfield, 2001).

community treatment orders

One of the more contentious elements of the revisions to the Mental Health Act (2007) is the concept of Supervised Community Treatment, which extends the range of coercion beyond the walls of the psychiatric institution. Specifically, patients detained in hospital under particular sections of the Mental Health Act can have conditions and restrictions applied to them upon discharge. Typically, their future freedom is made contingent upon their continuing to take their medication; if they do not comply, they can be forcibly returned to hospital. Less frequently, the order places other demands on the service user, such as regular attendance for outpatient appointments or residence at a specified address.

Community Treatment Orders (CTOs) allow psychiatric services to threaten service users with loss of liberty (in the form of a compulsory return to psychiatric hospital) unless they comply with the prescribed treatment. The implications of this piece of legislation is that law-abiding people with mental health problems, who typically retain the wherewithal to make their own informed decisions by, for example, weighing up the pros and cons of long-term use of antipsychotic medication, can be compelled to co-operate with drug treatment – treatment which may achieve little or no benefit and which is likely to evoke unpleasant side effects – or face forced incarceration in a psychiatric hospital.

The proposal to introduce CTOs activated much opposition from both service-user and professional organisations, including the Royal College of Psychiatry (Moncrieff, 2003). Despite these protestations, the government introduced this piece of legislation in November 2008 and, perhaps not surprisingly, the indications are that psychiatrists have grown fond of them. A comprehensive review of studies exploring stakeholder satisfaction with CTOs concluded that the psychiatrists surveyed (over 500 in total from the USA, Canada and New Zealand) gave 'broad support' to their use within the psychiatric system (Churchill et al., 2007, p. 88) with between 66 and 80 per cent reporting that they found them useful.

If the frequency with which they are deployed is an indicator of their popularity, it is reasonable to conclude that psychiatrists within the United Kingdom harbour a similar affinity with CTOs. Since their inception in 2008, the rate of implementation in England and Wales has grown steadily with almost 4,800 being executed in 2011–12, a 10 per cent increase compared to the previous year (Health and Social Care Information Centre, 2013). Furthermore, it has been formally acknowledged that there is an overuse of CTOs with ethnic minority groups: between 2008 and 2012, black people comprised 15 per cent of the CTO population as compared to their 2.9 per cent representation in the general population (Care Quality Commission, 2012).

Despite the infringement of human rights intrinsic to the implementation of CTOs, their advocates would have a stronger argument if outcome measures indicated that service users accrued some benefits from their utilisation. Evidence to date suggests this is not the case. A wide-ranging review, incorporating nine different studies that evaluated the effects of CTOs across a variety of outcome measures (including patient satisfaction, hospital readmission rates and length of hospital stays) concluded that there was a lack of evidence for any benefits for service users (Churchill et al., 2007).

Given the combination of human rights violations and lack of effectiveness, it is difficult not to concur with the conclusion of Morgan and Felton (2013) that the implementation of CTOs was politically motivated. However, it is likely that the policy-makers were, perhaps inadvertently, swayed both by their acceptance of the psychosis–violence stereotype and the spurious claims by biological psychiatrists that 'schizophrenia' is a disease that can be cured by rectifying a biochemical imbalance in the brain via medication compliance (see Chapter 2, p. 17).

advance decisions

An advance decision is a legal instrument that allows mentally competent adults to indicate, in a legally binding way, a particular treatment they do not wish to receive should they, at some time in the future, lose the wherewithal to make their own informed decisions. The origin of the advance decision concept was not the Mental Health Act, but a different piece of legislation called the Mental Capacity Act (2005). An advance decision offers people the power to shape and curtail future service responses if their health problems should render them incapable of making their own decisions (a mind state technically referred to as 'lacking capacity').

Unsurprisingly, the option of completing an advance decision (or 'advance directive' as it was known prior to the Mental Capacity Act) seems to appeal to service users with recurrent mental health problems who welcome the opportunity it affords to be treated like a responsible and active participant in future interactions with services (for a review, see Sidley, 2012). Furthermore, best practice guidance for clinicians endorses the value of giving service users with schizophrenia the opportunity to complete advance decisions so as to shape the way they are managed by services should they suffer an acute psychotic episode and thereby lose capacity (National Institute for Health and Care Excellence, 2009). Mental health professionals would risk prosecution were they to ignore an advance decision and continue to provide an intervention against the expressed wishes of a service user; it would be synonymous with proceeding with a treatment without the recipient's consent, an act that is explicitly prohibited within the professional guidelines of all clinicians working in health and social care services.

Alas, this empowering piece of legislation about advance decisions within the Mental Capacity Act is corrupted by the Mental Health Act; if a person is receiving treatment while under a section of the Mental Health Act, that person's expressed wishes (even when enshrined in a validly composed advance decision) can be overridden by the 'responsible clinician' who, in almost all cases, is a psychiatrist. The upshot of this further example of legalised discrimination is a curious anomaly. Any citizen can draw up an advance decision to, for example, withhold life-saving treatment for a specified medical emergency, and these wishes would have to be respected by the clinical team even if the inevitable consequence was death. In contrast, an advance decision to refuse a specific treatment for mental disorder – for example, not to be administered a particular antipsychotic medication – can be overruled if the psychiatrist chooses to section the patient under the auspices of the Mental Health Act.

The potential for advance decisions to be ignored by professionals may partly explain their under-utilisation within mainstream psychiatric services (MacPherson et al., 2008; Sidley, 2012), and there is some evidence that the prevalent 'doctor knows best' culture may act as a barrier to their completion (Swanson et al., 2003; Henderson et al., 2010).

Szmukler (2010) persuasively argued that the central reason for the discriminatory practices enshrined in the Mental Health Act was that the pathway for its development was independent from capacity-based law (in Britain, the Mental Capacity Act). Having two separate pieces of mental health legislation operating in parallel results in markedly different criteria for coercion to accept treatment: physical treatment can be imposed only if the patient lacks capacity and the treatment is deemed to be in the patient's best interests, whereas treatments for mental health problems can be legally enforced if the recipient is deemed to have a mental disorder and is assessed as being a risk to self or others. Buried within the Mental Health Act legislation is the fallacious assumption that the existence of mental disorder will always equate to the loss of capacity, to not being a full, autonomous person.

the powerless role of a psychiatric patient

Western societies are prone to ignore the social context when seeking explanations for a person's difficulties and assume that the cause lies within the individual. When someone reports or displays unusual experiences (for example, hearing voices that no one else can hear or expressing beliefs that seem bizarre or illogical) this individualist culture makes sense of such phenomena in terms of some inferred, internal deficit (Coles, 2013). In practice, the person struggling with unusual experiences is forced to choose between either accepting the dominant psychiatric view that they have a biochemical imbalance in their brains, or rejecting this conclusion and risking the subsequent coercion into treatment or loss of support. Inevitably, feeling overwhelmed and vulnerable, many service users will passively accept the explanations being offered by psychiatric experts.

People with mental health problems will usually have endured disempowering experiences in their earlier lives that render them incapable of resisting these professional overtures. Furthermore, there is an expanding body of evidence to suggest that these earlier life experiences may have directly contributed to the emergence of their mental health problems. For example, childhood abuse (physical or sexual) is a strong predictor of future voice hearing (Tyler, 2002; Read, Hammersley & Rudgeair, 2007), and growing up in socially and economically deprived environments may predispose to paranoia (Cromby & Harper, 2009).

Having been rendered symptomatic, vulnerable and powerless by previous adverse experiences, psychiatric experts enter the scene and assign diagnoses to the service users that act both to formalise their impotent position in society and to attribute the source of their difficulties to internal defects. Although diagnostic classifications have long been recognised as invalid and virtually meaningless (for a review, see Bentall, 2009, pp. 89–109), their simplicity is seductive, as is the veneer of scientific respectability they offer. Thus, if a service user displays extreme suspiciousness and mistrust of others, the psychiatric professional can label the individual as suffering from 'paranoid schizophrenia' and prescribe antipsychotic medication to rectify the assumed biochemical imbalance, thereby eliminating any need to try to understand the complex web of life experiences that will have shaped that person's perception of the world.

Despite psychiatric diagnoses failing to reliably differentiate between different groups of patients (for example, those labelled as suffering schizophrenia and bipolar disorder) and despite these labels being poor predictors of response to treatments, psychiatrists continue to pursue their mission to expand the number of human problems 'diagnosed' as a mental illness and, by doing so, to narrow the range of what is acceptable (Conrad, 2007).

Historically, their diagnostic tentacles have enveloped around an assortment of assumed illnesses, including: 'masturbatory insanity' (requiring surgical interventions to remove the clitoris or to sever the dorsal nerve to the penis); homosexuality (a phenomenon that was not de-medicalised until the 1970s); 'drapetomania' (to explain why some nineteenth-century slaves attempted to escape from their masters); and 'sluggish schizophrenia' (used to discount the political views of Russian dissidents) (Fernando, 1991; Summerfield, 2001). The colonisation of more and more common human reactions as illnesses continues unabated: the most recent edition of the *Diagnostic and Statistical Manual of Mental Disorders* (*DSM-5*), published by the American Psychiatric Association (2013), lists 15 more disorders than its predecessor, including grief following the death of a loved one – so, according to this brand of psychiatric wisdom, if you are still upset two weeks after a bereavement you have a mental illness.

the increasing use of coercion

As more and more behaviours and utterances have submitted to a mental illness categorisation – with the subsequent disempowerment of the individual so labelled, and the number of consultant psychiatrists available to administer their distinctive brand of benevolent paternalism more than doubling since 1980 (Brockington & Mumford, 2002; Royal College of Psychiatrists, 2011) – one might reasonably expect the need for coercion to be a rare occurrence. On the contrary: over recent years the use of force within mental health services has steadily risen. In 2011–12 this upward trend continued, the number of detentions under the auspices of the Mental Health Act increasing to 48,600 in England and Wales, a five per cent rise on the previous year (Health and Social Care Information Centre, 2013). As already mentioned, there have been similar rises in the use of Community Treatment Orders.

One of the few encouraging developments in psychiatric services over the last decade or so has been the expressed intention to promote 'recovery-orientated' practices, with the service users given greater opportunity to determine their own idiosyncratic routes towards achieving a more worthwhile and meaningful life (Repper & Perkins, 2012). It is therefore paradoxical that at the same time as mental health organisations are badging themselves with the recovery approach, their patients are encountering coercion on an escalating scale (Morgan & Felton, 2013).

In Western psychiatric services, there are a variety of approaches routinely enacted by professionals to ensure patients conform to the prescribed treatments. A framework proposed by Szmukler and Appelbaum (2008) captures the range of devices deployed to achieve compliance. At one end of the spectrum is persuasion, an appropriately collaborative approach whereby the professional discusses the pros and cons of the treatment options in the context of the patient's value system. The next rung of the ladder of influence involves interpersonal leverage where the psychiatric professional relies on the quality of the existing relationship with the service user to encourage compliance – the 'Will you take this medication for me?' approach.

If these first two strategies fail to achieve co-operation, the level of coercion is amplified and less egalitarian measures are brought to bear in the form of: inducements (for example, 'I'll be able to support your benefit application if you agree to take your medication'); threats ('I'll have no option but to section you if you continue to refuse to take your medication'); and coercion (the actual sectioning of a patient under the Mental Health Act to enforce treatment compliance). Justification of this level of force typically highlights risk issues, to self or others, despite evidence that psychiatric risk assessments are only slightly more accurate than those created by chance (Doyle & Dolan, 2002).

power disparities in multidisciplinary teams

Misuse of power is not restricted to professional–patient interactions. Although the idealised version of psychiatric multidisciplinary teams comprises a number of skilled professionals (psychiatric nurses, social workers, occupational therapists, psychiatrists and psychologists) working in harmonious collaboration for the benefit of the service user, the reality is often profoundly different, with power unevenly distributed and consultant psychiatrists exercising a level of influence grossly disproportionate to their skill set.

The power that an individual or group can exercise within an organisation is determined by a number of factors (Handy, 1993). Power can be acquired from several sources, including: resource power (derived from the privilege of controlling funding and other assets); position power (the influence implicit to a formal role, such as a manager or appointed team leader); expert power (vested in someone because of their acknowledged expertise); and personal power (linked to someone's charisma and personality).

All professionals working in a multidisciplinary team potentially benefit from every one of these four power sources, but psychiatrists typically enjoy privileged access to resource, positional and expert power. They are habitually nominated by senior managers to lead service redesign initiatives, investing them with more power than colleagues from other disciplines to determine which services are pruned and which are developed (an example of resource power). Similarly, mental health trusts in the UK National Health Service are required by law to appoint a consultant psychiatrist as a 'medical director' to sit on the Trust Board, the most influential forum within an organisation, a privilege not afforded to all professional groups (DHSS, 1984; Department of Health [DH], 1989) and therefore an example of a statutory requirement to preferentially invest positional power to medical personnel.

But arguably the most potent contributor to the power differentials in multidisciplinary teams is expert power. The skew towards 'illness like any other' approaches to mental health problems, ubiquitous across senior and middle managers (and the majority of clinicians, including non-medical personnel, working in psychiatric services), ensures that the psychiatrist is often perceived as the unique repository of the specialist skills required to work effectively with people with mental health problems.

Unsurprisingly, psychiatrists have embraced their role as the natural leaders of multidisciplinary teams with aplomb, as illustrated by their frequent assertions that they hold 'ultimate clinical responsibility' for all the psychiatric patients they see. It is commonplace within psychiatric services for psychiatrists (and other clinicians) to enquire as to who is the 'Responsible Medical Officer', a reference to a past era when the medical practitioner was assumed to have responsibility for patients at all times.

The source of this misapprehension seems to be confusion between professional responsibility (a duty of care to act in the interest of service users, within the limits of one's competence) and legal responsibility (the requirement to comply with statutory obligations when one is formally identified as the Responsible Medical Officer, or Responsible Clinician to use the terminology of the current Mental Health Act) (DH, 2010). A Responsible Clinician has been delegated the overall responsibility for a patient detained under a section of the Mental Health Act; for patients not compulsorily detained (the vast majority of psychiatric patients) an assertion to hold ultimate responsibility for a patient's care will always be invalid and meaningless.

It is unsurprising that many psychiatrists are confused on this matter. Despite holding (in common with all other professional groups) a circumscribed skill set, formal advice from organisations that represent medical professionals has at times colluded with the ultimate-responsibility myth. For example,

> Doctors alone amongst healthcare professionals must be capable of regularly taking ultimate responsibility for difficult decisions in situations of clinical complexity and uncertainty, drawing on their scientific knowledge and well developed clinical judgement patterns, and increased multi-disciplinary working should not alter this basic principle.
> (Academy of Medical Royal Colleges: Consensus statement on the role of the doctor – cited in DH, 2010, p. 14)

Such mendacious guidance has typically had general hospital settings in mind, where the notion of medical primacy acquires much more legitimacy. Reassuringly, with regards to mental health settings, sensible clarification has been offered: 'Clearly no discipline can claim to have exclusive competences for [team leadership] as a consequence of their professional training' (DH, 2005, p. 46). The primary remaining challenge is for service managers and mental health professionals (including consultant psychiatrists) to understand this statement and to begin to act in a way consistent with it.

references

American Psychiatric Association (APA). (2013). *The Diagnostic and Statistical Manual of Mental Disorders* (5ᵗʰ ed.). Arlington, VA: American Psychiatric Association.

Bentall, R.P. (2009). *Doctoring the Mind: Why psychiatric treatments fail.* London: Penguin.

Brockington, I.F. & Mumford, D.B. (2002). Recruitment into psychiatry. *British Journal of Psychiatry, 180,* 307–12.

Care Quality Commission (CQC). (2012). *Monitoring the Mental Health Act in 2011/12.* Retrieved 8 October 2014 from http://www.cqc.org.uk/sites/default/files/documents/monitoring-the-mental-health-act-in-2011-12-full-report.pdf

Churchill, R., Owen, G., Singh, S. & Hotopf, M. (2007). *International Experience of Using Community Treatment Orders.* London: Institute of Psychiatry.

Coles, S. (2013). Meaning, madness and marginalisation. In S. Coles, S. Keenan & B. Diamond (Eds.), *Madness Contested: Power and practice* (pp. 42–55). Ross-on-Wye: PCCS Books.

Conrad, P. (2007). *The Medicalization of Society: On the transformation of human conditions into treatable disorders.* Baltimore, MD: Johns Hopkins University Press.

Cromby, J. & Harper, D. (2009). Paranoia: A social account. *Theory and Psychology, 19*(3), 335–61.

Department of Health (DH). (1989). *Working for Patients.* London: HMSO.

Department of Health (DH). (2005). *New Ways of Working for Psychiatrists.* Royal College of Psychiatrists, National Institute for Mental Health in England. Retrieved 8 October 2014 from http://eprints.nottingham.ac.uk/788/1/NWW_Psychs.pdf

Department of Health (DH). (2010). *Responsibility and Accountability: Moving on from New Ways of Working to a creative, capable workforce.* Best Practice Guidance. National Mental Health Development Unit. Retrieved 8 October 2014 from http://www.rcpsych.ac.uk/pdf/Responsibility and Accountability Moving on for New Ways of Working to a Creative, Capable Workforce.pdf

Department of Health and Social Security (DHSS). (1984). *Griffiths Report: NHS Management Inquiry Report.* Retrieved 8 October 2014 from http://www.nhshistory.net/griffiths.html

Doyle, M. & Dolan, M. (2002). Violence risk assessment: Combining actuarial and clinical information to structure clinical judgements for the formulation and management of risk. *Journal of Psychiatric and Mental Health Nursing, 9*(6), 649–57.

Fernando, S. (1991). *Mental Health, Race and Culture.* London: MIND Publications.

Handy, C. (1993). *Understanding Organizations* (4th ed.). London: Penguin Books.

Health and Social Care Information Centre. (2013). *Inpatients Formally Detained in Hospitals under the Mental Health Act, 1983 and Patients Subject to Supervised Community Treatment, Annual Report, England, 2011/12.* Retrieved 8 October 2014 from http://www.hscic.gov.uk/catalogue/PUB12503/inp-det-m-h-a-1983-sup-com-eng-12-13-rep.pdf

Henderson, C., Jackson, C., Slade, M., Young, A.S. & Strauss, J.L. (2010). How should we implement psychiatric advance directives? Views of consumers, caregivers, mental health providers and researchers. *Administration and in Policy Mental Health, 37*(6), 447–58.

Laing, R.D. (1985). *Wisdom, Madness and Folly: The making of a psychiatrist.* New York: McGraw-Hill.

Macpherson, R., Hovey, N., Ranganath, K., Uppal, A. & Thompson, A. (2008). NICE guidelines on treating schizophrenia – an audit. *The Psychiatrist, 32,* 75.

Mental Capacity Act. (2005). Retrieved 8 October 2014 from http://www.legislation.gov.uk/ukpga/2005/9/contents

Mental Health Act. (1959). Retrieved 9 December 2014 from http://www.legislation.gov.uk/ukpga/Eliz2/7-8/72/contents

Mental Health Act. (1983). Retrieved 21 April 2014 from http://www.legislation.gov.uk/ukpga/1983/20/contents

Mental Health Act. (2007). Retrieved 14 April 2013 from http://www.legislation.gov.uk/ukpga/2007/12/contents

Moncrieff, J. (2003). The politics of a new Mental Health Act. *British Journal of Psychiatry, 183,* 8–9.

Morgan, A. & Felton, A. (2013). From constructive engagement to coerced recovery. In S. Coles, S. Keenan & B. Diamond (Eds.), *Madness Contested: Power and practice* (pp. 56–73). Ross-on-Wye: PCCS Books.

National Institute for Health and Care Excellence (NICE). (2009). *Schizophrenia: Core interventions in the treatment and management of schizophrenia in adults in primary and secondary care.* London: National Institute for Health and Care Excellence.

Read, J., Hammersley, P. & Rudgeair, T. (2007). Why, when and how to ask about childhood abuse. *Advances in Psychiatric Treatment, 13,* 101–10.

Repper, J. & Perkins, R. (2012). Recovery: A journey of discovery for individuals and services. In P. Phillips, T. Sandford & C. Johnston, (Eds.), *Working in Mental Health: Practice and policy in a changing environment* (pp. 71–80). Oxford: Routledge.

Royal College of Psychiatrists. (2011). *Census 2011*. Retrieved 16 October 2013 from http://www.rcpsych.ac.uk/pdf/Census Results 2011.pdf

Sidley, G.L. (2012). Advance decisions in secondary mental health services. *Nursing Standard, 26*(21), 44–8.

Summerfield, D. (2001). Does psychiatry stigmatize? *Journal of the Royal Society of Medicine, 94*, 148–9.

Swanson, J.W., Swartz, M.S., Hannon, M.J., Elbogen, E.B., Wagner, H., McCauley, B.J. et al. (2003). Psychiatric advance directives: A survey of persons with schizophrenia, family members and treatment providers. *International Journal of Forensic Mental Health, 2*, 73–86.

Szasz, T.S. (1973). *The Manufacture of Madness: A comparative study of the Inquisition and the mental health movement*. London: Routledge & Keegan Paul.

Szmukler, G. (2010). *How Mental Health Law Discriminates Unfairly Against People with Mental Illness*. Retrieved 16 October 2013 from http://www.gresham.ac.uk/lectures-and-events/how-mental-health-law-discriminates-unfairly-against-people-with-mental-illness

Szmukler, G. & Appelbaum, P. (2008). Treatment pressures, leverage, coercion and compulsion in mental health care. *Journal of Mental Health, 17*(3), 233–44.

Szmukler, G. & Holloway, F. (2000). Reform of the Mental Health Act: Health or safety? *British Journal of Psychiatry, 177*, 196–200.

Tyler, K.A. (2002). Social and emotional outcomes of childhood sexual abuse: A review of recent research. *Aggression and Violent Behavior, 7*, 567–89.

United Nations. (2006). *United Nations Convention on the Rights of Persons with Disabilities*. Retrieved 18 October 2013 from http://www.un.org/disabilities/default.asp?id=274

Vassilev, I. & Pilgrim, D. (2007). Risk, trust and the myth of mental health services. *Journal of Mental Health, 16*, 347–57.

part II: who is in charge here?

'I am the doctor; let me treat my patient the way I think fit.'

'Under no circumstances do I ever want to take haloperidol again; it makes me feel like I'm dying a slow, painful death,' said Joe to his community psychiatric nurse, shortly after discharge from hospital following his third psychotic episode.

Joe, a 40-year-old teacher, had suffered recurrent mental health problems for over 10 years. An intelligent man, he was employed as head of mathematics at the local comprehensive school and lived with Linda, his supportive wife. Despite always feeling inferior to his work colleagues, and generally lacking self-confidence, Joe's first contact with psychiatric services did not occur until he was 29 years old, when a particularly stressful time at school (involving external inspectors sitting in on his classes) triggered a period of voice hearing and paranoia. During this first psychotic episode, as with subsequent ones, the voices would persistently criticise him, branding him 'pathetic' and 'inadequate', and suggesting that his work colleagues were ridiculing him. At these times, Joe would become inconsolable and would scream at the voices to leave him alone and, occasionally, would accuse his fellow teachers of conspiring against him. Such anguish and misery had precipitated his most recent admission to an inpatient psychiatric unit.

Joe had told his community psychiatric nurse, Carol, on previous occasions that he did not think that one of the drugs used on the ward agreed with him. He described how after taking haloperidol he would always experience an intolerable combination of agitation and physical paralysis, subjectively feeling agitated but also enduring the sensations of being trussed in a drug-induced 'strait-jacket'. At these times Joe described how he also found it difficult to speak, owing to a feeling of rigidity in his jaw and tongue.

Such side effects are commonly reported by service users who have been prescribed haloperidol. This particular medication is classified as a 'typical' neuroleptic, one of a number of drugs used for the treatment of psychotic symptoms and mania. Common recognised side effects of this group of drugs include muscle stiffness, dry mouth, sluggishness and tremor. With ongoing use, haloperidol can cause a movement disorder called tardive dyskinesia, characterised by facial twitches, involuntary tongue movements and lip-smacking, a syndrome that may persist even after stopping the drug. There are now many antipsychotic medications available as alternatives to haloperidol, including a newer group of 'atypical' drugs that have a different side-effect profile.

Following his most recent admission to hospital, where Joe had again been prescribed haloperidol and had suffered the same side effects, he met with Carol and asked whether there was any way to ensure that he avoided being prescribed haloperidol in the future. During a psychotic episode his level of agitation and distress typically reached such heights that he was rendered incapable of making rational decisions, in this case to refuse the offer of haloperidol. Helpfully, Carol had introduced Joe and Linda to the potential value of completing an advance decision, a legally binding instrument that would allow Joe to refuse a specified treatment in the future should he lose capacity to make his own decisions. Both Joe and Linda expressed enthusiasm about the prospect of avoiding the prescription of haloperidol should Joe have further psychotic episodes, and Carol helped them to complete an advance decision form in which Joe stated that, 'Under no circumstances do I want to take haloperidol as it causes me horrendous side effects.' The form was signed by Joe and witnessed by Carol and, with Joe's consent, a copy of the form was placed on the electronic clinical record so that any professional accessing Joe's notes would immediately be alerted to the fact that an advance decision to refuse treatment existed for this patient.

Twelve months later, Joe suffered another psychotic episode and was admitted to a psychiatric hospital where the medical team, regardless of the advance decision, prescribed haloperidol. Linda was furious and immediately submitted a formal complaint about her husband's treatment.

Subsequent multidisciplinary reviews of Joe's care and management, along with the parts of the report that were shared by the external investigator into Linda's complaint, revealed that the sequence of events surrounding Joe's recent hospital admission was as follows.

It had been a frenetic time at Joe's school, with examinations looming. During a revision class, Joe had been verbally abused by one of his pupils. The incident reactivated all Joe's doubts about his competence as a teacher and he had struggled to sleep for four successive nights. Consequently, Joe's voice hearing returned, criticising and mocking, and in the early hours of a Monday morning Joe had become so distressed and agitated that Linda had persuaded her husband to accompany her to the accident and emergency department of the local hospital where he was assessed by the on-call psychiatrist and admitted to the acute psychiatric ward.

Carol, Joe's 'care co-ordinator' (the professional responsible for overseeing and organising the services a patient receives), was notified of Joe's admission when she arrived for work at the community mental health centre on a Monday morning. In keeping with standard practice, Carol attended the hospital ward the next morning to participate in a meeting to review Joe's progress.

When Carol arrived for the meeting, already present were the ward sister, the consultant psychiatrist, a junior doctor and Linda. (Over recent years it has become customary to invite the nearest relative to a patient's review meeting.) Upon entering the room, Carol had greeted Linda but, unusually, had only received a stilted, monosyllabic response; Carol noticed that Linda appeared flushed and agitated.

The junior doctor opened the meeting. 'Joe presented to A&E, accompanied by his wife, at 2.00 am on the morning of Monday 16th April. Assessment revealed that, over the previous seven days, Joe had experienced auditory hallucinations of escalating frequency and intensity. He had also become more suspicious of the people around him. At interview he was highly agitated, oscillating between self-condemnation and accusations that other people were trying to discredit him. With some persuasion he agreed to come into hospital for a few days as an informal patient so as to allow us to stabilise him.'

The consultant psychiatrist, who until this point had been reading his handwritten clinical notes, now interjected. 'Clearly this represents a relapse of his paranoid schizophrenic illness. We know from our previous experience with this patient how to best manage these episodes. To his existing medication regime of olanzapine and paroxetine, I have added haloperidol, 10 milligrams, three times per day.'

Carol observed that Linda inhaled deeply at this point, as if about to say something, and then glanced towards her.

'Since his admission,' continued the ward sister, 'Joe's agitation has reduced and he has not expressed any more paranoid ideas. He is, however, refusing to get out of bed this morning to attend this review.'

'I've just been in to see him,' said Linda, trying hard to conceal her anger. 'He can barely speak. Why have you given him that awful drug again?'

'Haloperidol is a very effective antipsychotic,' said the consultant psychiatrist, 'and we know from past experience that it is the quickest way of controlling Joe's schizophrenic illness.'

'Were you aware that Joe had completed an advance decision to refuse haloperidol?' asked Carol.

There was an awkward silence, during which the ward sister and psychiatrist glanced at each other, as if expecting the other to respond to the comment. It was the consultant psychiatrist who spoke first. 'Something was mentioned about some form or other being completed, saying he doesn't like taking haloperidol. But I'm sure you would agree that a few temporary side effects are a price worth paying for a speedy resolution of his psychotic illness and the torment associated with it.'

'But it was my understanding that it was against the law to disregard an advance decision,' said Linda.

'I'm sure Dr Munton acted in your husband's best interests,' said the ward sister.

'Best interests!' said Linda, no longer able to contain her frustration. 'He's tormented now, lying in bed like a zombie. The only difference is that he is unable to express it because his jaw and tongue have seized up due to that damn medication.'

'We can give your husband other medication to get rid of any side effects,' said the consultant psychiatrist, 'but you have to understand that I am the doctor here and I have a professional responsibility to treat each of my patients in the way I deem fit so as to alleviate the mental illness as quickly as possible.'

Within one hour of leaving the review meeting, Linda submitted a formal complaint against the consultant psychiatrist to the hospital managers, specifically highlighting his flagrant disregard of her husband's advance decision to refuse haloperidol. As Joe was a voluntary patient, to ignore his explicit wishes expressed in a valid advance decision was an illegal act that rendered the practitioners concerned liable to litigation. Intriguingly, the day after the complaint, the consultant psychiatrist compulsorily detained Joe on Section 3 of the Mental Health Act (confining him to hospital for a period of six months for treatment), an action difficult to justify on clinical grounds as Joe had shown no inclination to leave the ward. Being sectioned did however legitimise the continued use of haloperidol against Joe's expressed wishes, at least from a legal perspective; persistence with haloperidol when there are multiple alternatives available would be impossible to justify on 'best practice' criteria.

The details of the formal investigation into Linda's complaint were not made public. Linda did, however, receive a formal apology from the managers and an acknowledgement that professional staff had made a mistake in disregarding her husband's advance decision. No formal disciplinary action was taken against any member of staff – an unsurprising outcome, given that the threshold for sanctions against medical consultants seems appreciably higher than that applied to staff from other professions.

'you must not see the psychologist anymore'

I noticed that something was wrong the instant Graham entered my office. His cheeks emitted a pinkish glow and he lacked his usual vibrancy, the absence of introductory chitchat being particularly striking. I asked him if everything was OK, as he did not seem himself.

'The psychiatrist has told one of my patients that she must not see me anymore,' said Graham, 'and he is going to make a formal complaint against me.'

Graham was a qualified clinical psychologist employed in an Early Intervention Service (commonly referred to as 'EI'), a speciality within mental health provision that provides support and interventions to young people experiencing their first episode of psychosis. Compared to mainstay psychiatric services, EI typically offers a less medicalised view of mental health problems, normalising a person's unusual experiences and conveying optimism about the prospects of recovery. Nevertheless, as with other teams, the established posts for the EI service comprised a multidisciplinary group of psychiatric nurses, social workers, psychiatrists and psychologists. However, at the time, no psychiatrist was in post owing to recruitment difficulties – the philosophy of this EI team did not correspond to the cherished beliefs of most psychiatrists – so the medical input for the EI service users was sourced from a consultant psychiatrist employed within the local community mental health team. My role at the time was as acting manager of the EI team, and Graham was one of the people I line-managed.

Lengthy discussion with Graham revealed that the backdrop to the psychiatrist's displeasure concerned a young, female patient who had been attending weekly sessions with Graham for the purpose of psychological therapy to reduce the distress associated with her voice hearing. Alongside this input, the patient would attend the psychiatrist's outpatient clinics on a monthly basis to review and monitor her antipsychotic medication. During a recent session with the psychiatrist, the patient had been told that she was afflicted with a severe and enduring mental illness and would be required to take the medication for the remainder of her life. This bleak prophecy had triggered a sense of hopelessness in the patient and three days later she arrived for her psychology session in a highly distressed state, a presentation that contrasted sharply with her steady improvement over the previous six months. Graham had decided that it would be appropriate for him to meet with the psychiatrist to discuss the patient's sensitivities to any references suggesting that her life might not improve in the future, and to inform him of the patient's strong emotional reaction following her recent outpatient appointment with him. Unfortunately, despite multiple attempts to arrange a meeting with him, and repeatedly leaving messages with his secretary requesting he returns his calls, the psychiatrist did not respond. So Graham wrote a letter to the psychiatrist, providing a further update of the psychological work as well as incorporating a reference to the patient's anguish following her last outpatient appointment.

Graham's letter had been professionally written with a conciliatory tone throughout. In contrast, the copy of the psychiatrist's response to Graham, which landed on my desk the following morning, constituted a tirade of epic proportion. In the letter the psychiatrist complained that Graham had: 'tried to dictate how the patient should be managed'; shown 'arrogance' in suggesting how future communications with the patient might be delivered so as to reduce the likelihood of triggering feelings of hopelessness; conducted a risk assessment of the patient that was 'at best ... amateurish' and 'filled with breathtaking errors' in that it 'put too much emphasis on what the patient told you'; independently initiated psychology sessions with the patient; and had demonstrated that his 'working practices and boundaries' were flawed and a cause of great concern.

I gathered further information from both Graham and his clinical supervisor (a more experienced clinical psychologist who regularly explored Graham's work) and closely inspected the relevant communications relating to the patient in question. My conclusion was that Graham had acted appropriately, and with integrity, in relation to the patient and his communications with the psychiatrist. I wrote to the psychiatrist and refuted each of his assertions in turn: Graham had shared a psychological formulation with the multidisciplinary team that suggested helpful ways of communicating with the patient (rather than arrogantly dictating how she should be managed); the risk assessment had been competently conducted, and we made no apology for giving weight to what the patient said; whether to proceed with psychological therapy was a decision appropriately determined by the patient, after discussion with the psychologist; there was no evidence of Graham's clinical practice being flawed and, unless he had any concrete evidence to the contrary, he should formally withdraw his scurrilous allegation.

Stalemate prevailed, with neither side shifting their position and the interchanges growing more acrimonious. The service director (the most senior manager in the adult mental health service) arranged a formal meeting to be attended by the psychiatrist, the lead psychiatrist, Graham and me. After we had regurgitated our polarised positions, the nub of the disharmony revealed itself.

'So which bit of my response to your complaints do you not accept?' I asked the psychiatrist, somewhat provocatively. 'Is it the legitimacy of sharing a formulation, the validity of the risk assessment or the appropriateness of a clinical psychologist proceeding with therapy without your prior permission?'

The psychiatrist's jaw clenched and he glared in my direction. 'I'm tired of having to say the same thing again and again. Maybe the key question here concerns the role of the Responsible Medical Officer, and the authority inherent in the role.'

'You seem to be challenging the right of other professions to exercise a degree of autonomy in their day-to-day work,' I said. 'I trust that in a modern, twenty-first-century mental health service you are not claiming ultimate clinical responsibility for the work of other professionals in the team?'

'I am the Responsible Medical Officer ....'

'That term is meaningless, as the patient in question is a voluntary one,' I said.

The psychiatrist's face flushed, and a dribble of drying spittle oozed from one side of his mouth. 'Then I will section her this afternoon,' he said.

The lead psychiatrist grimaced. The service director stared in disbelief.

Following the meeting, the service director instructed the psychiatrist to fully retract, in writing, his allegation questioning Graham's clinical practice or face formal disciplinary action. In 33 continuous years of employment in the National Health Service, this was the only occasion I witnessed a senior manager officially censure a psychiatrist for his or her behaviour towards non-medical colleagues.

leadership skills? it's in the genes!

When discussing issues pertaining to clinical leadership of multi-disciplinary teams with a psychiatrist colleague (a personable and caring man who always did his best for the service users), he broadly acknowledged that it was dubious for any professional to automatically assume such a role. He did, however, qualify his response by saying that he believed that medical practitioners had inherent 'sapiential' skills and knowledge which often rendered them effective clinical leaders. As I did not understand what was meant by the term 'sapiential', and not wishing to appear stupid in the eyes of a respected colleague, I did not seek clarification at the time.

Later, I consulted my Collins English Dictionary and discovered that the definition of sapiential was: 'showing, having or providing wisdom'. So his assertion was that psychiatrists have intrinsic wisdom which makes them natural clinical leaders; maybe it is not only mental illness that they believe resides in our genes!

let the doctors and nurses treat you

part I: passivity and submissiveness

People who experience mental health problems have typically endured life events (trauma, abuse, social and economic deprivation) that rendered them powerless and helpless (see Chapter 4, pp. 67–8). Already predisposed to view their world as one over which they can effect little influence, traditional psychiatry confronts them with a paradigm that promotes passivity and compliance.

This chapter will explore how biological models of mental disorder encourage a submissiveness in service users that acts as a significant impediment to recovery. The second section of the chapter will share detailed anecdotes from the real-world psychiatric arena to illustrate these unhelpful practices in action.

the stymying consequences of medical-model explanations

The 'illness like any other' approach to mental health problems asserts that the imperative goal of therapeutic intervention is to rectify an assumed imbalance in the service user's brain biochemistry. It is easy to see how an assumption of inherent biological defect, fundamental to medical-model explanations of emotional distress, discourages service users from adopting an active role in their treatment programmes; thus, if a patient has been identified as displaying some clear organic pathology (for example, a blockage in a cardiac artery or a tumour in the bowel) the patient would be well advised to obediently follow the expert administrations of the physicians and passively accept the treatments offered. Traditional psychiatric practice strives to achieve such conformity amongst its service users.

There is evidence from the literature to suggest that medical model accounts of mental health problems serve to promote this lack of agency. A study by Fisher and Farina (1979) reported that undergraduate students who had been given a biogenetic explanation of the development of mental disorders were more likely to conclude that they had less potential to control these problems as compared to another student group who had been exposed to psychosocial accounts of aetiology. Similarly, Birchwood et al. (1993) found that patients who accepted their 'schizophrenia' diagnoses (and, presumably, the biological illness status associated with it) perceived themselves to possess less control over their mental disorders.

A perception of negligible influence over current emotional difficulties would be expected to discourage efforts to change, as it is futile to invest energy into something outside of our control. In recognition that such a view might nurture helplessness and despondency, Birchwood and colleagues proposed that the symptoms of depression (a common accompaniment to psychosis) might be linked to this perception of no control. Furthermore, there is evidence that people are more likely to misuse drugs and alcohol as a means of moderating their distress when they believe their mental health problems have a biogenetic basis (Fisher & Farina, 1979).

The stress–vulnerability model of mental disorder, extensively referred to by clinicians within routine psychiatric practice, may be distinctively potent in evoking passivity among service users. First applied to mental health by Zubin and Spring (1977) as a framework for explaining recurrent psychotic episodes in people with a schizophrenia diagnosis, the stress–vulnerability model proposes that the timing of the emergence of symptoms of mental illness will depend upon an interaction between an acquired vulnerability and the current level of stress in a person's life. According to the model, if someone has a high level of pre-existing vulnerability, it would only require a moderate degree of day-to-day stress to precipitate an episode of mental illness. On the contrary: if someone has very little predisposition, huge life pressures would be necessary to risk rendering the individual mentally ill.

Although Zubin and Spring originally described 'acquired vulnerability' as originating from a range of factors that included past life experiences (trauma, family disharmony, negative life events), in contemporary psychiatric practice the model is generally corrupted to assume that predisposition has an exclusively genetic basis. As bluntly described by Read, Mosher and Bentall (2004), the version of the stress–vulnerability concept deployed is not seeking an integration of approaches, but 'a colonization of the psychological and social by the biological' (p. 4). Psychosis sufferers and their relatives are often provided with 'psycho-education' (Dixon et al., 2001) which peddles the message that the patient inherited some degree of genetic defect confering vulnerability that could be activated by stress at any time. Given such an explanation for their previous mental health problems, it is understandable why service users might avoid life's challenges and opt for passivity.

For those service users labelled as displaying 'schizophrenia', the concept of negative symptoms might lead professionals and family members to expect inactivity. Negative symptoms are commonly claimed to be an inherent component of schizophrenia, and include apathy, anhedonia (an inability to experience pleasure) and blunting of emotions. If these symptoms are assumed to be natural manifestations of the mental illness, there is a risk that others may collude with the service user's withdrawal from life.

However, it remains contentious as to whether negative symptoms constitute a core component of psychosis or merely represent a combination of medication side effects and the consequent helplessness of suffering a severe mental disorder (Barnes & Paton, 2011). There is evidence that negative symptoms can improve when the dosage of antipsychotic drugs is reduced (Seidman et al., 1993). Other commentators have suggested that they represent an enduring form of post-traumatic stress disorder, resulting from earlier abuse and victimisation (Stampfer, 1990).

why is passivity a hindrance?

It could be argued that a period of passive withdrawal would often be desirable, even essential, following the onset of severe emotional distress. The opportunity of an interlude for recuperation, away from the demands of everyday life, might be appealing at times of psychological pain, and the original idea of the lunatic 'asylum' fostered the value of this form of respite. Although such an argument is not without merit – time in a sanctuary often representing a necessary first step of a person's journey of recovery from mental health problems – extended episodes of passivity are usually counterproductive. The specific reasons for this will now be discussed.

passivity as an impediment to the recovery process

Over the last 15 years or so the desirability of mental health services adopting what is termed a 'recovery approach' has been increasingly emphasised both in government policy (Department of Health [DH], 2004, 2006) and in the practices of innovative clinicians (for example,

Repper & Perkins, 2012). In these contexts, recovery is not primarily about the elimination of symptoms of mental illness, but the adherence to a set of values and principles that have been shown to enable people with mental health problems to achieve worthwhile lives.

A number of researchers have asked service users to identify the key characteristics involved in their journeys of recovery from mental health problems, and all have testified to the importance of being proactive. Thus, Andresen et al. (2003, p. 586) constructed a conceptual model of recovery and proposed that one of the central processes entailed 'taking responsibility'. Similarly, Farkas (2007, p. 70) highlighted the value of 'discovering a more active sense of self', while Davidson and Strauss (2011), on the basis of interviews with people struggling to recover from prolonged psychiatric disorders, championed the need for the service user to adopt a more active and collaborative role. Furthermore, a recent review of the recovery literature in the United Kingdom identified 'meaningful occupation' as one of the four core components of a recovery approach (Stickley & Wright, 2011, p. 253).

A willingness to adopt an active approach facilitates recovery in a general sense, enabling the pursuit of valued roles (with regards to education, work and leisure) and the reintegration into social networks (Repper & Perkins, 2012). In a recovery-orientated service it is the people with mental health problems who are viewed as possessing expert knowledge about their strengths and cherished life goals, and there is an expectation that they lead the recovery journey and, in so doing, control their own destinies. The 'illness like any other' approach, prevalent within traditional psychiatric services, unhelpfully encourages service users to continue to take their medication and wait for the anticipated improvements. Clearly, such an approach promotes passivity and acts as an impediment to recovery.

passivity as an impediment to psychological therapies
Psychological therapy (often referred to as 'talking therapy') constitutes the main alternative to medication as an intervention within psychiatric services, although limited access continues to be recognised (Centre for Mental Health, 2006). The effectiveness of psychological therapies has been demonstrated for a wide range of mental health problems, including depression, anxiety and psychosis (National Institute for Health and Care Excellence [NICE], 2013). Despite attracting legitimate criticism for their propensity to give insufficient emphasis to social context in the development and maintenance of mental health problems (for example,

Coles, Diamond & Keenan, 2013), psychological therapies are popular with service users.

There are many varieties of psychological therapy, each with its own band of expert advocates and each with a distinctive focus. The most common types include cognitive-behaviour therapy (primarily targeting a person's beliefs and behaviours), person-centred therapy (using the relationship with the therapist to promote personal growth), cognitive-analytic therapy (elucidating repeated and problematic patterns of behaviour towards others), and psychodynamic psychotherapy (promoting insight into the way early experiences have shaped current functioning). Irrespective of which approach is used, if any benefit is to accrue from the enterprise, it is imperative that the service user enters into a collaborative relationship with the therapist and is willing to engage in self-exploration. Two prerequisites for success in therapy, therefore, are a belief that one can influence one's own future wellbeing and a readiness to put effort into doing so. If a person has already been sold the idea that mental health problems are primarily caused by defects in brain biochemistry it is improbable that either of these imperatives will be evident.

passivity as an impediment to overcoming depression
While passivity is likely to impede progress with any form of psychological therapy, its detrimental impact may be most obvious when a person is depressed. To acquire a diagnosis of depression requires the presence of either persistent low mood or loss of interest in daily activities, together with some other signs such as insomnia, loss of energy, concentration difficulties and feelings of guilt or worthlessness (American Psychiatric Association [APA], 2013). Given that withdrawal and lack of interest in life are core features of the disorder, it is understandable that people suffering depression might often adopt a passive approach to treatment, taking their antidepressant medication as instructed by their psychiatrists and waiting for an upturn in their mental wellbeing.

Rather than viewing inactivity as a key symptom of depression, in the 1970s psychologists began to propose that this change in behaviour was the cause of the disorder. Behavioural models of depression were developed that argued that depression is a direct result of a reduction in 'positive reinforcement' – the enjoyment and pleasure we generally experience from our day-to-day activities and routine interactions with other people (Lewinsohn & Libet, 1972; Ferster, 1973; Lewinsohn & Graf, 1973). More recently, an approach referred to as 'behavioural activation' has been proposed as an appropriate treatment for depression, based on the assumption that avoidance functions to deny depressed people access to potential sources of reinforcement (Jacobson et al., 1996).

In clinical practice, behavioural approaches are sold to depressed service users on the basis that depression makes everything more effortful so the person does less, but this reduced activity then exacerbates the depression. Following logically from this model, the depressed individual is encouraged to gradually reintroduce activities that previously were associated with pleasure or a sense of mastery. Using diary sheets (referred to as 'activity schedules'), these specific tasks are agreed as home assignments for the depressed person to attempt between therapy sessions. Every effort is made to ensure successful completion by only setting realistic targets.

Although simplistic in its conceptualisation of depression, research has shown that interventions based on a behavioural model can be an effective treatment for many sufferers. Reconfiguring a depressed person's daily schedule so as to selectively reward non-depressed behaviours (such as going to a local shop) rather than depressed behaviours (such as staying in bed all day) – a procedure known as contingency management – was found to be slightly more effective than antidepressant medication in a group of outpatients (McLean & Hakstian, 1979). An alternative behavioural approach, involving the teaching of social skills, proved to be as effective as either antidepressant medication or brief dynamic psychotherapy with a sample of depressed women (Hersen et al., 1984).

Cognitive-behaviour therapy, the most widely available talking treatment, teaches a range of self-help skills to change deleterious styles of thinking and typically includes a combination of cognitive strategies (for example, examining the evidence for and against negative thoughts so as to challenge their validity) and behavioural strategies (for example, activity scheduling). Jacobson et al. (1996) demonstrated that the behavioural activation component of the treatment package, which strives to enable depressed people to reclaim active participation in their own lives, produced as much benefit as the full cognitive-behavioural programme. Remarkably, a study by Dimidjian et al. (2006) reported that behavioural activation achieved greater benefits than cognitive-behaviour therapy for more severely depressed patients, while matching the effects of antidepressant medication in reducing acute distress.

The same investigators (Dobson et al., 2008) followed up this group of patients and compared the relative efficacy of behavioural activation, cognitive-behaviour therapy and antidepressant medication in preventing recurrence of depression. They discovered that behavioural activation and cognitive-behaviour therapy were each more effective in reducing the risk of depressive relapse as compared to a group who had been treated with medication but then withdrawn onto a placebo pill (where the patients believed they were continuing to take an antidepressant but were, in fact, ingesting an inert substance). Furthermore, over a two-year follow-up period, there was no significant difference between the potency of behavioural activation and cognitive-behavioural therapy in protecting against further episodes of depression.

Physical exercise per se appears to confer advantage with regards to susceptibility to depression. Camacho et al. (1991) found that a higher level of physical activity at the start of the study predicted less depressive episodes over subsequent years, even after controlling for other depression risk factors (including negative life events, socio-economic deprivation and inadequate social networks). Similar findings were reported by Strawbridge et al. (2002) in their study of almost 2,000 older people (aged 50 or above) who were followed over a five-year period. Their central conclusion was that exercise was protective for depression irrespective of whether a disability was present.

Considering the evidence as a whole, it is clear that a dynamic approach to life, involving exercise, community engagement in rewarding activities and the overcoming of avoidances, promotes and maintains wellbeing. As such, the passivity inherent to an 'illness like any other' approach to mental health problems is deeply unhelpful.

the benefit system paradox

The powerful American mental illness advocacy and carers organisation, the National Alliance on Mental Illness (NAMI), is strident in its endorsement of the 'illness like any other' approach to mental health problems and the corresponding entitlement of sufferers to claim state benefits, as illustrated by the following statement from their website:

> Persons with a serious mental illness are just as entitled to disability payments as persons with a serious physical illness. If you or your relative has a mental illness such as schizophrenia, obsessive-compulsive disorder, manic depression, or another disabling brain disorder (mental illness), you may be entitled to benefits from the Social Security Administration.
> (NAMI, 2013)

At first reading, the statement above might be viewed as an egalitarian endorsement of the rights of people with mental health problems; indeed, anyone challenging the 'illness like any other' approach risks accusations of a lack of compassion or (particularly in the USA) of being branded a scientologist. Yet additional payments contingent upon the presence of reversible psychiatric disorders will potentially act as a perverse disincentive to recovery, more so when the financial benefit is not time limited.

Until recently, Disability Living Allowance (DLA) constituted the most pertinent benefit for people under 65 with mental health problems in the United Kingdom. As the name suggests, DLA is targeted at people who are anticipated to be disabled (due to physical or mental ill health) for a substantial period of time. There are two components to DLA, 'care' and 'mobility', each of which is assessed separately. According to the NHS Choices website (2013) (a comprehensive, internet information service), the care component is paid to people who require 'attention' or 'supervision'. An example given on the website of a person needing attention is that of 'making sure that someone with a mental health disability takes their medication'. Supervision is associated with 'keeping an eye on somebody to ensure that they do not put themselves or others in danger'. With regards to the mobility component, agoraphobia (an irrational fear of leaving a place of safety, typically one's home) is offered as a disorder that would confer eligibility.

The care component of DLA is paid at three levels, the 2013 rates ranging from £21 to £79 per week (GOV.UK, 2013a). The mobility component is paid at two levels, either £21 or £55 per week (at 2013 rates). Furthermore, if a person is eligible for DLA, a friend or family member may be able to claim a 'carer's allowance' for looking after them.

From April 2013 the government began a process of replacing DLA with another benefit, the Personal Independence Payment (PIP), although it is anticipated that many existing DLA claimants will remain on the old benefit until 2015 (GOV.UK, 2013b). While the naming of the new benefit suggests a shift in policy from one of supporting disability to one of promoting independence, the criteria to assess eligibility for PIP sound broadly similar to those used for DLA. Thus, the 'daily living' component is contingent upon a long-term health problem that leads to difficulties with basic daily tasks such as cooking, maintaining personal hygiene, washing, interacting with others, managing money and 'managing your medicines and treatments'. Also similar to its predecessor, the 'mobility' component will be given for 'help with going out or moving around' (GOV.UK, 2013b).

Passivity, as previously discussed, is associated with an array of disadvantages for a person recovering from mental health problems. The provision of open-ended financial incentives for persistence of psychiatric disorders such as depression, psychosis and anxiety (conditions that have no enduring biological cause and which are essentially reversible) only risks installing a further barrier to recovery.

It is a huge irony that a society where disempowerment and marginalisation contribute significantly to the development of mental disorder (Coles, 2013) then administers financial incentives to those so afflicted that inevitably act to maintain their isolation and disengagement from life. Would this public money not be more sensibly deployed to fund a marked expansion in change-enablers (support groups, safe houses for crisis management, education, work opportunities, peer support, community initiatives) rather than introducing a perverse financial penalty (loss of benefit) for defeating one's mental disorder?

references

American Psychiatric Association (APA). (2013). *Diagnostic and Statistical Manual of Mental Disorders* (5th ed.). Arlington, VA: American Psychiatric Association.

Andresen, R., Oades, L. & Caputi, P. (2003). The experience of recovery from schizophrenia: Towards an empirically validated stage model. *Australian and New Zealand Journal of Psychiatry, 37*(5), 586–94.

Barnes, T.R.E. & Paton, C. (2011). Do antidepressants improve negative symptoms of schizophrenia? *British Medical Journal, 342,* d3371.

Birchwood, M., Mason, R., MacMillan, F. & Healey, J. (1993). Depression, demoralisation and control over psychotic illness. *Psychological Medicine, 23,* 387–95.

Camacho, T.C., Roberts, R.E., Lazarus, N.B., Kaplan, G.A. & Cohen, R.D. (1991). Physical activity and depression: Evidence from the Alameda County study. *American Journal of Epidemiology, 134*(2), 220–31.

Centre for Mental Health. (2006). *We Need to Talk: The case for psychological therapies on the NHS.* Mental Health Foundation. Retrieved 8 October 2014 from http://www.centreformentalhealth.org.uk/pdfs/we_need_to_talk.pdf

Coles, S. (2013). Meaning, madness and marginalisation. In S. Coles, S. Keenan & B. Diamond (Eds.), *Madness Contested: Power and practice* (pp. 42–55). Ross-on-Wye: PCCS Books.

Coles, S., Diamond, B. & Keenan, S. (2013). Clinical psychology in psychiatric services: The magician's assistant? In S. Coles, S. Keenan & B. Diamond (Eds.), *Madness Contested: Power and practice* (pp. 111–20). Ross-on-Wye: PCCS Books.

Davidson, L. & Strauss, J.S. (2011). Sense of self in recovery from severe mental illness. *British Journal of Medical Psychology, 65*(2), 131–45.

Department of Health (DH). (2004). *Essential Shared Capabilities: A framework for the whole of the mental health workforce.* London: HMSO.

Department of Health (DH). (2006). *From Values to Action: The Chief Nursing Officer's review of mental health nursing.* London: HMSO.

Dimidjian, S., Hollon, S.D., Dobson, K.S., Schmaling, K.B., Kohlenberg, R.J., Addis, M.E. et al. (2006). Randomized trial of behavioral activation, cognitive therapy, and antidepressant medication in the acute treatment of adults with major depression. *Journal of Consulting and Clinical Psychology, 74*, 658–70.

Dixon, L., McFarlane, W.R., Lefley, H., Lucksted, A., Cohen, M., Falloon, I. et al. (2001). Evidence-based practices for services to families of people with psychiatric disabilities. *Psychiatric Services, 52*, 903–10.

Dobson, K.S., Hollon, S.D., Dimidjian, S., Schmaling, K.B., Kohlenberg, R.J., Gallop, R. et al. (2008). Randomized trial of behavioral activation, cognitive therapy, and antidepressant medication in the prevention of relapse and recurrence in major depression. *Journal of Consulting and Clinical Psychology, 76*(3), 468–77.

Farkas, M. (2007). The vision of recovery today: What it is and what it means for services. *World Psychiatry, 6*(2), 68–74.

Ferster, C.B. (1973). A functional analysis of depression. *American Psychologist, 28*, 857–70.

Fisher, J. & Farina, A. (1979). Consequences of beliefs about the nature of mental disorders. *Journal of Abnormal Psychology, 88*, 320–7.

GOV.UK. (2013a). *Personal Independence Payment (PIP).* Retrieved 6 November 2013 from https://www.gov.uk/pip/eligibility

GOV.UK. (2013b). *Simplifying the Welfare System and Making Sure Work Pays.* Retrieved 6 November 2013 from https://www.gov.uk/government/policies/simplifying-the-welfare-system-and-making-sure-work-pays/supporting-pages/introducing-personal-independence-payment

Hersen, M., Bellack, A.S., Himmelhoch, J.M., & Thase, M.E. (1984). Effects of social skills training, amitriptyline, and psychotherapy in unipolar depressed women. *Behavior Therapy, 15*, 21–40.

Jacobson, N.S., Dobson, K.S., Truax, P.A., Addis, M.E., Koerner, K., Gollan, J.K. et al. (1996). A component analysis of cognitive-behavior treatment for depression. *Journal of Consulting and Clinical Psychology, 64*, 295–304.

Lewinsohn, P.M. & Graf, M. (1973). Pleasant activities and depression. *Journal of Consulting and Clinical Psychology*, *41*, 261–8.

Lewinsohn, P.M. & Libet, J. (1972). Pleasant events, activity schedules and depression. *Journal of Abnormal Psychology*, *79*, 291–5.

McLean, P.D. & Hakstian, A.R. (1979). Clinical depression: Comparative efficacy of outpatient treatments. *Journal of Consulting and Clinical Psychology*, *47*, 818–36.

National Alliance on Mental Illness (NAMI). (2013). *Social Security Benefits*. Retrieved 21 April 2014 from http://www.nami.org/Content/ContentGroups/Helpline1/Social_Security_and_Disability_Benefits.htm

National Institute for Health and Care Excellence (NICE). (2013). Retrieved 21 April 2014 from http://www.nice.org.uk/guidancemenu/conditions-and-diseases/mental-health-and-behavioural-conditions

NHS Choices. (2013). *Benefits for the Person You Care for: Care components definitions*. Retrieved 21 April 2014 from http://www.nhs.uk/CarersDirect/moneyandlegal/disabilitybenefits/Pages/DisabilityLivingAllowance.aspx

Read, J., Mosher, L.R. & Bentall, R.P. (2004). 'Schizophrenia' is not an illness. In J. Read, L.R. Mosher & R.P. Bentall (Eds.), *Models of Madness: Psychological, social and biological approaches to schizophrenia* (pp. 3–7). London: Routledge.

Repper, J. & Perkins, R. (2012). Recovery: A journey of discovery for individuals and services. In P. Phillips, T. Sandford & C. Johnston (Eds.), *Working in Mental Health: Practice and policy in a changing environment* (pp. 71–80). Oxford: Routledge.

Seidman, L.J., Pepple, J.R., Faraone, S.V., Kremen, W.S., Green, A.I., Brown, W.A. et al. (1993). Neuropsychological performance in chronic schizophrenia in response to neuroleptic dose reduction. *Biological Psychiatry*, *33*(8–9), 575–84.

Stampfer, H. (1990). 'Negative symptoms': A cumulative trauma stress disorder? *Australian and New Zealand Journal of Psychiatry*, *24*(4), 516–28.

Stickley, T. & Wright, N. (2011). The British research evidence for recovery, papers published between 2006–2009 (inclusive). Part I: A review of the peer-reviewed literature using a systematic approach. *Journal of Psychiatric and Mental Health Nursing*, *18*, 247–56.

Strawbridge, W.J., Deleger, S., Roberts, R.E. & Kaplan, G.A. (2002). Physical activity reduces the risk of subsequent depression for older adults. *American Journal of Epidemiology*, *156*(4), 328–34.

Zubin, J. & Spring, B. (1977). Vulnerability: A new view of schizophrenia. *Journal of Abnormal Psychology*, *86*, 103–26.

part II: the debilitated must take it easy and follow instructions

wait for the antidepressants to 'kick in'

I felt upbeat at the end of the third session of psychological therapy with Denise. Despite her continuing to feel low in mood, self-critical, guilty and a pervasive sense of worthlessness, she had found our discussion about the factors that might have contributed to the onset and maintenance of her depression personally relevant and plausible. We had collaboratively developed a plan of action and Denise left my office with, for the first time since we met, a smidgen of hope and purpose. A week later, and 10 minutes into our fourth session, I experienced a crushing realisation that my previous optimism had been misplaced.

Denise was 45 years old, married, with two teenage daughters. She worked full time for the local council as an environmental health officer, a job that she had mostly enjoyed for the last 15 years. Denise had endured a difficult childhood, often being the victim of physical abuse at the hands of her drunken father. Despite this adversity, she had achieved excellent grades at school and had attended university, where she met her current husband. Apart from a brief period of postnatal depression after the birth of her first child, Denise had had no previous contact with psychiatric services.

Three months prior to my first contact with Denise, she had been persuaded by her husband to attend her general practitioner and seek help for her low mood and recurrent suicidal thoughts. Twelve months earlier, Denise's mother had died and this loss had disturbed her greatly, perhaps as a result of their shared experience of physical abuse forging a profoundly close relationship between them. Shortly after this bereavement, her younger daughter left home for university, thus compounding her sense of loss. Also, two weeks prior to her GP visit, there had been an incident at work where the owner of a fast-food restaurant verbally abused her after she had informed him that his establishment had failed to meet the required standards of hygiene. The cumulative effect of these negative life events was to trigger powerful emotions of self-loathing and despair. Concerned by Denise's comments that her life was not worth living, her GP had immediately prescribed antidepressant medication and referred her to the local community mental health team, where she was assessed by a psychiatrist and admitted to an inpatient unit for two weeks.

Following her discharge from hospital, Denise attended further sessions with the psychiatrist, Dr Jenkins, who formed the opinion that, although her inclinations to commit suicide had waned, she continued to suffer a 'depressive illness'. Based on this conclusion, the psychiatrist changed her medication, prescribing sertraline (one of a newer type of antidepressant) and referred her to me, the team clinical psychologist, to be considered for psychological therapy.

During my optimistic third session, we had sketched out how the maintenance of her current sadness and self-condemnation might result from an interaction between her thoughts, behaviour and feelings. Denise was on sick leave from work and this often triggered self-critical thoughts about letting her colleagues down, which in turn made her feel more depressed and guilty. To compound the situation, since her discharge from hospital she had been staying in bed for most of the day, a behaviour that exacerbated her negative thoughts about herself. By the end of this third session Denise expressed a commitment to take the first small steps to break out of the vicious circle where feeling depressed leads to less activity and, in turn, less activity leads to a strengthening of the her depressed feelings.

Our negotiated plan to increase her engagement in rewarding activities incorporated two elements. Firstly, each day she would schedule one task to complete (for example, walking to the local shop for bread and milk) and she would set her alarm and get out of bed progressively earlier to accomplish this daily task. Secondly, Denise agreed to phone her work manager at the council offices and accept his earlier offer of a graduated return to work, a process that would start in four weeks' time and involve her working three half-days per week in the first instance.

When I collected Denise from the waiting area for our fourth session it was immediately apparent that things had not gone well. She appeared more fidgety than on previous occasions, and avoided eye contact with me. As she took her seat in my office she began to weep.

'You're clearly very upset,' I said. 'Describe what has happened since our last meeting.'

'It's been an awful week,' said Denise, her voice faltering as she tried to hold back the tears. 'I've felt really down. And I think my husband's getting fed up of me, and I can't blame him; he's having to do everything at the moment.'

'How did you get on with the home tasks?'

'I'm really, really sorry,' said Denise. 'I've not completed any of the tasks we'd agreed. I got a bit confused.'

'That's OK, there's no need to apologise. I appreciate that when someone's feeling very low in mood, concentration can be a problem. I should have checked with you before you left the session that you were clear about what you were going to try and do.'

'No, I understood the tasks, and the reasons for doing them. It's just that ....'

Denise seemed reluctant to continue with her explanation. I waited until she felt able to do so.

'It's just that Dr Jenkins told me that I shouldn't overstretch myself at the moment.'

Further discussion revealed that, immediately following our previous psychological therapy session, Denise had attended an appointment with her psychiatrist, who occupied the office next door but one to my own.

'And what exactly did Dr Jenkins say?' I asked, neutrally, trying to hide my rising irritation.

'He increased the dose of my sertraline and told me I must take it easy and wait for the medication to kick in. He also said that I'm suffering with a severe depressive illness and shouldn't even think about returning to work for at least six months.'

Denise's confusion was palpable. Within a three-hour period at our community mental health centre she had, in one room, been sold the idea that inactivity and avoidance might now be maintaining her depression, only to be told an hour later, by another professional two doors down, that she must rest and wait for her biochemical deficiency to be rectified by the medication. So much for multidisciplinary working! It was remarkable that she chose to continue to attend a place where so-called experts espoused such contradictory messages.

'if I achieve more independence I'll lose my house'

Stephen was 52 years old and had worked throughout his adult life in a recruitment company until, four years before our meeting, he was made redundant. As a man with a strong work ethic, losing his job had shattered his self-esteem and precipitated an episode of profound depression and crippling anxiety. After two years of antidepressant medication, there had been some improvement in his mood, but he continued to experience anxiety about leaving home alone and therefore spent his days in isolation while his wife went to work. It was at this point he was referred to me, the team clinical psychologist.

I visited Stephen at his home for our initial meeting, as it was clear from the available information already on file that he would struggle to attend a community mental health centre on his own. During our first session, Stephen expressed embarrassment about his lack of independence. For the previous 18 months, the prospect of leaving home alone precipitated pronounced anxiety feelings and, as a consequence, during this period he had not been able to go out without his wife as a chaperone. Stephen identified his ultimate goal of therapy as to be able to leave his house alone and mix with people in the community without enduring feelings of panic.

Stephen's primary problem was one often referred to in professional circles as agoraphobia, a fear of leaving a place of safety. Any attempt to step across the threshold of his home, or even anticipation of doing so, would typically evoke escalating physiological arousal (heart pounding, sweats, rapid shallow breathing) and a range of threatening thoughts ('I will lose control and make a fool of myself'; 'I will collapse in the street'; 'I might go insane'). An essential component of effective psychological intervention for agoraphobia is graduated exposure to the feared situations, in this case being alone and outside of his home. So we collaboratively developed a hierarchy of his feared situations, beginning with a tentative first step (for example, walking alone to the end of his street and back) and culminating in a situation that generated extreme fear (for example, completing the weekly shop alone at a busy supermarket).

From the outset, Stephen showed himself to be a courageous and industrious collaborator in the psychological treatment programme. On the first day of therapy, he tentatively stepped outside his front door and accompanied me to the end of his street where we briefly separated, before returning home. This procedure was repeated, the time that Stephen spent on his own while outside his home being gradually extended. Despite at first feeling high levels of anxiety, Stephen stayed with these feelings (rather than escaping to the refuge of his home) until their intensity waned, thereby effectively challenging his threatening thoughts about losing control, collapsing or going insane. In the time between the therapy sessions, Stephen diligently carried out the 'homework' tasks, leaving his house alone on a daily basis as he successfully worked his way through his hierarchy of feared situations. In every respect, Stephen was an ideal recipient of psychological therapy, and his progress towards greater independence was swift.

But then the upward trajectory in his progress faltered. He cancelled a couple of planned sessions with me (sessions that were now taking place at the community mental health centre – a further reflection of the progress he had made), giving 'not feeling well' as the reason. Concerned that there may have been slippage in his progress, I organised a review session at Stephen's home.

'When we last met, five weeks ago, you had been making great progress,' I said. 'How have things developed since?'

'Not so good,' said Stephen, head bowed, 'I've really slipped back; I've not been out of the house for a fortnight. I'm so sorry.'

'There's no need to apologise,' I said. 'Following your rapid early progress, it sounds like you've hit a sticky patch. That's to be expected; overcoming difficulties such as these usually involves some ups and downs. Maybe we could look in detail at the point where things started to slip.'

Stephen appeared fidgety in his armchair, shifting his weight as if unable to find a comfortable position, in contrast to previous sessions where, particularly in the safety of his own home, he had presented as calm and unruffled – it was only the prospect of stepping across the threshold into the outside world that evoked anxiety.

'Following our last meeting, for two or three days I did well, leaving the house on my own each morning as planned and staying out until my anxiety had come down. But then one morning I decided not to go out; I didn't think it would do any harm to miss a day. But then the following day the prospect of going through the front door triggered a panic attack; I've not been out since.'

As is customary in cognitive-behavioural therapy, we discussed the underlying threatening thoughts that might have fuelled his panic and subsequent avoidant behaviour, trying to learn from the setback and aiming to get the intervention back on track as soon as possible. But Stephen interrupted this process.

'At our first meeting, I made a vow to myself that I would be totally honest with you. But there's another big concern that I have not told you about, one that I feel very ashamed of.'

Stephen's face had flushed crimson, and he stared down at his feet. I waited for him to continue.

'I'm really scared about what will happen if I lose my DLA. My wife's salary is not enough. Without my benefits we wouldn't be able to pay the mortgage and we would lose the house. I wouldn't be able to live with myself if that happened.'

Stephen went on to explain that, even if he did overcome his fears about leaving the home, the prospect of returning to full-time employment in the existing job market was remote; a 52-year-old man who had been unable to work for four years because of a mental disorder would not fare well where each vacancy attracted multiple applicants.

It was saddening to observe a proud man with a strong work ethic tormented with shame as he described the perverse option the social welfare system had given him: strive to overcome your fears and lose your house, the prized possession that Stephen and his wife had worked decades to attain, or continue with the agoraphobic problem and keep your house. If I had been in Stephen's position I think I know which option I would have favoured.

I thanked Stephen for his honesty, wished him contentment for the future and, by mutual agreement, we brought the psychological therapy to a close.

the nurses must wear uniforms!

The fourth item on the agenda of the steering-group meeting for a new rehabilitation unit read, 'Staff uniforms'. The forum comprised a couple of senior managers, the prospective manager of the proposed unit, the relevant psychiatrist and me (the psychology representative). Contrary to what one might expect from a meeting whose expressed purpose was to make decisions about how the new service should operate, it was immediately apparent that it had been predetermined that all staff employed in the proposed service would wear uniform; important decisions about mental health services in the NHS often emerge from private conversations between a senior manager and a psychiatrist outside of the formal planning forums. The reason the item had been included on the agenda was to discuss the type of tunic that should be worn on the new rehabilitation unit, rather than to debate whether uniforms per se were an appropriate way forward.

'I think we should go with the same uniform as worn on the acute inpatient wards,' said Andrea, a senior manager.

Despite my opposition, the nurses, male and female, on the psychiatric inpatient unit had been wearing blue for the previous 12 months. By so doing, they were indistinguishable from their colleagues on the medical and surgical wards of the adjacent district hospital who were dealing with cancers and heart diseases. I decided it would be irresponsible of me not to challenge this further example of a drift towards the 'illness like any other' approach, with all its associated disadvantages for people with mental health problems.

'Is staff uniform, of any kind, really appropriate for this rehabilitation unit, particularly in light of the service's central commitment to recovery principles?'

Silence prevailed. Those present fixed their gazes on the agenda papers, avoiding any eye contact with me, presumably interpreting my contribution as another example of psychology mischief-making. It was the psychiatrist who eventually spoke.

'Uniforms seem to have achieved a number of benefits on the inpatient unit.'

The three managers present all nodded in unison, apparently re-energised by the psychiatrist's comment.

'Yes, we've seen a 50 per cent reduction in the number of incidents on the inpatient unit,' said Karen, the other senior manager, implying that uniformed nursing staff had a sedating quality with regards to the patients, rendering them less inclined towards disturbed behaviour.

'Might that very welcome reduction in the number of incidents be more likely due to other factors, such as the recent recruitment of some excellent nursing staff to key posts?' I asked.

'And we've realised a 150 per cent reduction in the number of patients absconding from the ward,' said Karen, who was now on a statistical roll.

'Don't you think the recently installed airlock on the door might have something to do with that?' I said, recognising a rising sense of frustration within me (an all-too-familiar experience when participating in forums involving service managers).

'I remain convinced', said Andrea, 'that uniforms promote more respect from the patients as well as encouraging professional behaviour in our staff. Why are you so against the idea, Gary?'

The flippant answer would have been 'For the same reasons I gave the last time we discussed it', but I resisted this urge and tried to present the main arguments against the wearing of uniform on a rehabilitation ward.

'Are we not trying to encourage the residents within the new unit to take an active approach to their treatment, to lead and guide their own recovery journeys? To achieve this we need to empower our service users. After all, they are the experts; only they know what life experiences they've had, what thoughts and feelings play out inside them, and the details of their strengths, interests and valued goals. The wearing of a uniform inevitably introduces a power imbalance in the relationship; it indicates that the nurse is the expert, and the patient should be the passive recipient of her administrations. That's not the message we're trying to promote, is it?'

But as before, my protestations were futile. The decision had already been made. As with the large majority of NHS psychiatric service bosses, my two senior managers originated from the nursing profession and essentially clung to the view that a psychiatric nurse was no different to those working on general wards, delivering care to patients who were afflicted with illnesses. Perhaps I should have been grateful that white-coated doctors were not, as yet, strutting through the psychiatric wards with stethoscopes swinging from around their necks!

6

risk distortion and risk aversion

part I: bureaucracy and defensive practice

A striking paradox of Western psychiatric services concerns their approach to risk. While espousing a central mission of risk reduction, the fundamental tenets of the medical-model approach to mental health problems ensure that many recipients of psychiatric 'care' will suffer iatrogenic consequences, the obsession with risk existing hand-in-hand with the infliction of harm.

After reviewing the evidence for a link between mental disorders and risk (to self and others), the core risk assessment process within psychiatric services will be described. Reference will be made to the distortions and unrealistic expectations that lead to risk aversion, a culture of blame and the subsequent time-intensive bureaucratic processes. Finally, this section will examine how psychiatry has proffered mental illness as a valid excuse for violent crimes, thereby providing seductively simplistic explanations to support pleas of insanity and diminished responsibility in the court system.

The second part of this chapter will provide anecdotes to illustrate how risk aversion and wasteful bureaucracy are rife within current psychiatric services.

how risky are people with mental health problems?

The two main areas of risk routinely considered by psychiatric services are risk to self (chiefly addressing the potential for suicide or deliberate self-harm) and the risk to others (the potential to behave violently towards people with whom they have contact).

risk of suicide

In 2011, the official suicide figure for the United Kingdom stood at 6,045, with males outnumbering females by a ratio of over three to one (Office of National Statistics, 2013). Undoubtedly, this number underestimates the actual level: suicide is a legal verdict that will only be reached if there is unequivocal evidence that the person intended to end his or her life. Estimates of non-fatal deliberate self-harm suggest a much greater prevalence, surveys reporting that at least 5 per cent of the population have engaged in this behaviour at some point in their lives (Shaw-Welch, 2001; Hawton et al., 2002; Meltzer et al., 2002).

Between two-thirds and three-quarters of all people who commit suicide do not have a recognised mental disorder or previous contact with psychiatric services (Luoma, Martin & Pearson, 2002; Lee et al., 2008; Appleby et al., 2013). The factors associated with a heightened risk of suicidal behaviour are likely to be common to clinical and non-clinical populations. These include: previous acts of deliberate self-harm (Ovenstone & Kreitman, 1974; Kreitman & Foster, 1992); thoughts and expressions of suicidal intent (Harriss, Hawton & Zahl, 2005); socio-demographic parameters such as unemployment, low-status work, experience of violence (either as victim or perpetrator), the absence of a long-term partner, drug or alcohol misuse (Kreitman & Foster, 1992); under-developed skills in solving interpersonal problems (Schotte & Clum, 1987); hopelessness characterised by a perception that nothing positive will happen in the future (Fawcett et al., 1987; Beck, Brown & Steer, 1989; MacLeod et al., 1997); and difficulties managing and tolerating powerful emotions (Linehan, 1993).

On average, people receiving help from mental health services will display these risk factors to a higher degree than the general population and therefore constitute a group who are, overall, more inclined to engage in suicidal behaviour. A central reason for this association between psychiatric-patient status and vulnerability to suicide is that the risk factors for developing mental health problems overlap considerably with those that predispose a person to self-destruction. For example, social deprivation and disempowerment grossly inflate the likelihood of subsequently acquiring the diagnostic label of schizophrenia or depression (Harrison et al., 2001; Ritsher et al., 2001). Similarly, previous traumatisation powerfully predicts the emergence of auditory hallucinations – a prominent feature of psychosis (Bebbington et al., 2004; Read et al., 2005).

A further, more obvious, reason why suicidal people are more prevalent within the population of psychiatric patients is that risk to self is often a key factor that propels them into services, whether this is voluntarily or under the auspices of the Mental Health Act legislation.

Hopelessness is one of the most potent predictors of suicide; for example, even a modest level of hopelessness is a significant predictor of attempted suicide in a group of people suffering their first episode of psychosis (Klonsky et al., 2012). Clearly, the social deprivation, marginalisation and disempowerment that are commonplace in the emergence and maintenance of mental health problems can often stifle optimism about a better life. Furthermore, the detrimental impact of mental disorder on a person's educational and vocational opportunities can understandably lead to perceptions of a bleak future. (The additional dollop of hopelessness administered by our biologically skewed psychiatric services will be described in Chapter 7.)

risk of violence to others
While people suffering mental health problems display a much greater risk of deliberate self-harm and suicide as compared to the general population, evidence of an inflated propensity to engage in violence is weak and contradictory.

Investigations focusing on selected groups have sometimes found a relationship between mental disorder and violent acts. Hence, an American study of 17,000 prison inmates by Silver, Felson and Vaneseltine (2008) reported an unusually emphatic link between mental disorder and violence, concluding that a history of mental health problems was associated with violent assault, sexual offending and more deviant forms of criminal activity. Bentall and Taylor (2006) concluded that paranoid delusions occasionally lead to violent acts. In contrast, other studies of specific groups have failed to detect a connection. An overview of over 200 different investigations (referred to as a 'meta-analysis') found that the delusions and hallucinations of psychosis sufferers did not significantly predict violence in forensic populations (Douglas, Guy & Hart, 2009). Similarly, Appelbaum, Robbins and Monahan (2000) could find no convincing support for a causative link between paranoid delusions and violence.

General population studies consistently conclude that people who have acquired a mental illness diagnosis rarely commit murder. Only 5 per cent of all homicides are attributable to people labelled as schizophrenia sufferers, a figure dwarfed by alcohol and drug misuse which contribute to over 60 per cent of such cases (Shaw et al., 2006; Swinson et al., 2007). For all crimes, a Dutch study by Vinkers et al. (2012) calculated that only 0.07 per cent were directly attributable to mental health problems, many other factors (for example, socio-economic status and coexisting substance misuse) confounding the relationship between mental disorder and offending. The overall conclusion is that, although there may be a small association between some types of psychosis and a propensity to violence, mental health problems make only a slight contribution to the level of crime in society and, when they are implicated, the mental problems per se are rarely the crucial determinants.

Szmukler (2000) succinctly estimated that the risk of being murdered by a stranger with psychosis is about one in 10 million, on a par with being struck by lightning. Furthermore, people with mental health problems are much more likely to be the victims of crime than the perpetrators, one study reporting that those diagnosed with schizophrenia had a 14 times greater risk of being violently assaulted than of acting in the role of assailant (Brekke et al., 2001). Unfortunately, public perception does not reflect this reality; the media's portrayal of people with mental health problems as dangerous contributes to the maintenance of this distortion (Coverdale, Nairn & Claasen, 2002; Corrigan, Kerr & Knudsen, 2005; Thornicroft, 2006).

Perversely, risk in the context of mental health problems is construed, and responded to, in an entirely different way to the threats inherent in society as a whole. Those people afflicted with mental disorders are subject to a distinctive set of controls, legalised in the form of the Mental Health Act (see Chapter 4, pp. 62–5), that would be construed as an infringement of fundamental civil liberties, and resoundingly rejected, if applied to other sections of the community.

Pilgrim and Tomasini (2013) starkly illustrate how assumed risk is used to justify these discriminatory practices and how, on closer inspection, there is no logical rationale for these double standards. Thus, a person acting in a bizarre or unintelligible way risks incarceration without trial – psychiatry and other authorities typically arguing that the action is defensible on the grounds of reduced risk to both the individual and other people. But if risk reduction was the overarching driver of policy and legislation, it would make far more sense, as Pilgrim and Tomasini argue, to impose a weekend night-time curfew on teenagers and young adults, an action that would markedly reduce the number of violent incidents and unwanted pregnancies (but one that would, of course, be rejected in a civilised society as a violation of human rights).

From the late 1990s the British government has seemed uniquely inclined to try to use mental health legislation as a way of controlling people who are challenging and difficult (Freshwater & Westwood, 2006). In addition to the introduction of Community Treatment Orders (see Chapter 4, pp. 64–5), the Mental Health Bill, the precursor to the revisions of the Mental Health Act in 2008, invented a new mental illness of 'dangerous and severe personality disorder' (DSPD) as a vehicle for detaining problematic people who had not committed any criminal offence. The DSPD construct has no scientific validity (as is the case with other diagnostic labels) and clearly represents a politically motivated attempt to impose controls on troublesome people and, by doing so, to be seen to be the noble protector of the general public.

Inflated public perceptions of the risk posed to others by people with mental health problems, together with the perverse and discriminatory way that this risk is managed within our society, represents the context in which psychiatric services operate and might partly account for their obsessive approach to risk assessment.

risk assessment in psychiatric services

statutory requirements

The transition from the large asylums to community care corresponded to a growing culture of risk management within psychiatric services, encouraged by high-profile incidents of violence (such as the murder of Jonathan Zito in 1992) where mental health professionals were perceived to have failed to protect the public from mentally disturbed perpetrators (Szmukler, 2000; Morgan, 2007). The protracted discussions around the proposed reforms to the Mental Health Act, prior to their implementation in 2007, strengthened the perceived links between mental disorder and dangerousness and led to a government expectation that the risk a psychiatric patient poses to others should be routinely assessed.

In the United Kingdom, the central framework deployed by psychiatric services for the planning, delivery and evaluation of the support offered to each service user is referred to as the Care Programme Approach (CPA). Introduced in 1990, the CPA introduces a number of service requirements, including: the identification of a mental health professional to act in the role of 'care co-ordinator'; the comprehensive assessment of a patient's health and social care needs; the development of an individualised care plan; and formal reviews (within specified time limits) of the effectiveness of the input being offered (Department of Health [DH], 1999, 2008).

Since the inception of the CPA, the assessment and management of risk has been considered to be a core element of the process, and subsequent revision of the guidelines has placed greater emphasis upon the promotion of safety for service users and others. Thus, a Department of Health consultation document concerning proposed changes to CPA stated: 'Safe practice indicates that professionals and organisations should have robust systems that allow for valid, reliable and retrospectively defensible risk assessment and management for every service user' (DH, 2006, p. 22). Also introduced was an explicit distinction between 'enhanced' CPA (for those patients with multiple needs and higher levels of risk) and 'standard' CPA (where both needs and level of risk are less).

Consequently, contemporary psychiatric practice demands that the mental health professionals allocated the role of care co-ordinator are obliged to fill in a cumbersome array of risk assessment paperwork for each enhanced-CPA patient on their caseloads. Typically, each organisation dictates the specific forms and tick-box lists that need to be routinely completed. The paperwork addresses the various risk domains (suicide, violence, exploitation and vulnerability) and incorporates a combination of items covering the history of risky behaviours, the patient's expressed ideas and intentions, socio-demographic features, levels of drug and alcohol use, mood instability, hopelessness, ease of access to means of inflicting harms (such as sharp objects and stockpiled medication) and any other information, from whatever source, that might suggest an increased risk.

The bureaucratic burden of this endeavour has recently been recognised (Royal College of Psychiatrists [RCP], 2008). But how effective is this time-consuming risk assessment process with regards to reducing the likelihood of harm to self or others?

the accuracy of risk assessment
Although the risk assessments of psychiatric experts are often construed as objective facts and free of any value-laden bias (Lupton, 1999; Morgan & Felton, 2013), it is now widely recognised that they are blighted with inaccuracies and are unlikely to reduce the likelihood of the sort of high-profile incidents that attract such media attention (Witteman, 2004; Morgan, 2007). Statistically, it has been shown that the risk predictions of mental health professionals regarding the potential for harm to others are only marginally more accurate than those generated by chance (Doyle & Dolan, 2002). Assessments of risk to self are unlikely to be any more accurate; the National Confidential Inquiry into Suicide and Homicide by People with Mental Illness (Appleby et al., 2013) reported that, in over a quarter of UK suicides, the person had been assessed by psychiatric services in the 12 months prior to death and was deemed, at last contact, to display little or no risk.

The fundamental weakness of clinical risk assessments, for both risk to self and others, is their low specificity in that they identify many people as at risk who do not go on to engage in any suicidal behaviour or violence – referred to in the literature as 'false positives'. Accurate prediction about one individual's risk status is never going to be possible in relation to outcomes like suicide and homicide that are, thankfully, very rare. In illustration of this conclusion, Szmukler (2000) estimated that, even with the most comprehensive of risk assessments, for every homicide correctly predicted there would be at least 2,000 false positives.

Despite the ultimate futility of the task, research in the mental health domain has continued to strive for more precise risk prediction (RCP, 2008) while the clinicians are compelled to routinely complete ever more time-intensive risk assessments. What drives this unproductive enterprise? One potential explanation is a culture of blame (Morgan, 2007).

blame culture and defensive practice

A survey conducted by the Royal College of Psychiatry (2008) in the UK reported that 58 per cent of mental health professionals believed that the form-filling around risk assessment reflected defensive organisational practice rather than serving any clinical function. Risk-management practices within statutory services will inevitably be influenced by the prevailing political climate that determines what level of risk is acceptable. Unfortunately, throughout the last 20 years or so, politicians and much of the media seem to assume that untoward incidents are preventable, and that the occurrence of an adverse event must entail an error in professional practice (Szmukler, 2000). In this context of unreasonable societal expectations, statutory mental health organisations strive to avoid the inevitable bad publicity, or possible sanctions, associated with the unexpected death of a service user. In turn, the clinicians typically endure the completion of the risk assessment paperwork, not because of its clinical utility, but so as to protect themselves from blame if an untoward event should occur.

A preoccupation with risk to others has led to a concern for public safety trumping the welfare of people with mental health problems, evoking complaints from psychiatrists that they are expected to act as 'agents of social control' (RCP, 2008, p. 21). Yet the preventative detention of many as a means of avoiding one major adverse event, while incongruous with a democratic society, may constitute an acceptable compromise between civil liberties and public protection in the minds of many of the general public (Morgan, 2007).

In this risk-averse context that permeates psychiatric provision in the National Health Service, each serious incident (such as a suicide, act of serious self-harm, episode of violence or a homicide) is automatically followed by a formal investigation. At the local level these take the form of a 'post-incident review' (PIR) led by a senior manager; homicides by people with mental health problems will trigger a public inquiry. Although professing to represent an opportunity for learning and subsequent service improvement, the underlying assumption embedded within these investigations is that the adverse event was preventable and therefore someone should be held accountable.

The distorted retrospective, characteristic of public inquiries into homicides by people with mental illness, has attracted much criticism. For example, Szmukler (2000) berates the way that the patient is assumed to have no agency whatsoever in the sequence of events preceding the incident and how, with hindsight, the negative outcome can appear inevitable when the investigative process is shorn of the multitude of choice points involved in forward-moving time. Furthermore, Szmukler highlights the futile practice whereby the inquiry focuses on the existing requirements on a service (typically whether designated forms or other CPA obligations were completed) irrespective of whether these specifics had any bearing on the outcome; many mental health professionals will be familiar with chastisements emanating from this source. Although Szmukler's critique addressed public inquiries, the issues highlighted are equally applicable to all levels of formal investigation conducted within services.

While psychiatrists often lament the political pressure upon them to act as agents of social control, it is difficult not to conclude that their 'illness like any other' model encourages the expectation, from both the government and the general public, that risk inherent in those with mental health problems can and should be externally managed. After all, if extreme or incomprehensible behaviour is a direct consequence of disturbances in brain biochemistry and faulty genes, people with mental disorders should not be held responsible for their actions. This paternalistic approach to those (and only those) deemed to have a 'mental illness' finds expression within the court system.

insanity as an excuse for violent crime

A fundamental tenet of Anglo-American law is that a person is only guilty of a crime if two conditions are satisfied. Firstly, a criminal act must have been committed, referred to as the 'actus reus'. Secondly, at the time of the offence the person must have had a criminal mind, referred to as the 'mens rea'. This second requirement for evil intent dates back to the thirteenth century and offers the opportunity for the defence counsel to try to excuse a crime on the basis of insanity. Currently, an insanity defence is recognised in England and Wales and in most American states.

Since the early eighteenth century, there have been fluctuations in the relative influences afforded legal and medical experts in shaping the court's decisions regarding the degree to which insanity pleas should mitigate punishment (Reznek, 1997). A pivotal ruling occurred in 1843 when the House of Lords attempted to define insanity in what later became known as the M'Naghten rules. There had been a public outcry when a Bethlem psychiatrist, Dr Munro, successfully argued that Daniel M'Naghten, who had shot the Prime Minister's private secretary, was guilty of no crime as his mental illness was 'sufficient to deprive the prisoner of all self-control' (cited in Reznek, 1997, p. 19). According to the M'Naghten rules, the insanity excuse for wrongdoing is only valid if a person suffers a mental affliction to such a degree that it is impossible for that person to distinguish right from wrong.

In the aftermath of the M'Naghten rules, the battleground between legal and medical specialists has mainly concerned the evidence required to legitimately conclude that a person's mental disorder reasonably excuses wrongdoing. Most psychiatrists argued that behaviour is mainly determined by physiological events and therefore not amenable to wilful control. Diamond (1962) provided a stark expression of this medical-model viewpoint in the claim that 'Within 10 years biological and physiological tests will be developed that will demonstrate beyond a reasonable doubt that a substantial proportion of our worst and most vicious criminal offenders are actually the sickest of all' (cited in Reznek, 1997, p. 4). In contrast, the legal paradigm assumed that people are essentially self-governing, their behaviour explicable in terms of their beliefs and desires.

In the 1950s in the District of Columbia (USA) a court ruling, now referred to as the 'Durham rule', proposed that the existence of a mental illness was sufficient to excuse a defendant. Adoption of the Durham rule would effectively remove the ultimate decision-making about guilt or innocence from the jury and into the hands of a specialist psychiatrist. Predictably, it was popular with the psychiatric profession but attracted much criticism from other sources for its liberal definition of legal insanity, many believing that criminal responsibility could best be determined by a properly informed jury unfettered by expert testimony. The Durham rule has been ignored by most jurisdictions.

The question of whether someone is not guilty for reason of insanity (often referred to as NGRI) invites a categorical, all-or-nothing answer and, as such, resonates with the paradigm of traditional psychiatry that construes mental illness as a distinct, biological entity whose presence or absence can be reliably determined. In contrast, the less-rigid concept of 'diminished responsibility' was introduced into English law in 1957 as a partial defence that, if successful, may lessen the subsequent sentence (Reznek, 1997). Sensibly it allows juries, after consideration of all the evidence (circumstances surrounding the offence, background information, and testimony as to the defendant's state of mind), to conclude that criminal responsibility was substantially impaired.

The concept of diminished responsibility, alongside the rejection of the Durham rule, has led to 'expert' testimony being reduced to one source of evidence for the jury to consider in determining the level of criminal responsibility. This seems eminently sensible. Arbitrary and invalid diagnostic labels, purporting to inform the jury as to whether or not the defendant had a mental illness, should not be relied upon when deliberating over the degree of criminal responsibility; to do so represents a lazy and simplistic way of making sense of a criminal act and discourages the nuanced exploration of each case on its own merit. A wise justice system will strive for a comprehensive understanding of each individual's unique situation (taking into account the person's past experiences, beliefs, emotions, relationships and external environment) before making decisions that impact substantially on people's lives. If only our psychiatric services displayed such sagacity!

references

Appelbaum, P., Robbins, P. & Monahan, J. (2000). Violence and delusions: Data from the MacArthur Violence Risk Assessment Study. *American Journal of Psychiatry, 157*(4), 566–72.

Appleby, L., Kapur, N., Shaw, J., Hunt, I.M., While, D., Flynn, S. et al. (2013). *The National Confidential Inquiry into Suicide and Homicide by People with Mental Illness Annual Report.* Centre for Mental Health and Risk, University of Manchester.

Bebbington, P.E., Bhugra, D., Brugha, T., Singleton, N., Farrell, M. et al. (2004). Psychosis, victimisation and childhood disadvantage: Evidence from the second British National Survey of Psychiatric Morbidity. *British Journal of Psychiatry*, *185*, 220–6.

Beck, A.T., Brown, G. & Steer, R.A. (1989). Prediction of eventual suicide in psychiatric inpatients by clinical ratings of hopelessness. *Journal of Consulting and Clinical Psychology*, *57*, 309–10.

Bentall, R.P. & Taylor, J. (2006). Psychological processes and paranoia: Implications for forensic behavioural science. *Behavioural Sciences and the Law*, *24*, 277–94.

Brekke, J.S., Prindle, C., Bae, S.W. & Long, J.D. (2001). Risks for individuals with schizophrenia who are living in the community. *Psychiatric Services*, *52*, 1358–66.

Corrigan, P.W., Kerr, A. & Knudsen, L. (2005). The stigma of mental illness: Explanatory models and methods for change. *Applied and Preventive Psychology*, *11*(3), 179–90.

Coverdale, J., Nairn, R. & Claasen, D. (2002). Depictions of mental illness in print media: A prospective national sample. *Australian and New Zealand Journal of Psychiatry*, *36*(5), 697–700.

Department of Health (DH). (1999). *Effective Care Coordination in Mental Health Services: Modernising the care programme approach – a policy booklet.* London: HMSO.

Department of Health (DH). (2006). *Reviewing the Care Programme Approach: A consultation document.* Care Services Improvement Partnership.

Department of Health (DH). (2008). *Refocusing the Care Programme Approach. A policy and positive practice guidance.* London: HMSO.

Diamond, B. (1962). From M'Naghten to Currens and beyond. *California Law Review*, *50*, 189–205.

Douglas, K., Guy, L. & Hart, S. (2009). Psychosis as a risk factor for violence to others: A meta-analysis. *Psychological Bulletin*, *135*, 679–706.

Doyle, M. & Dolan, M. (2002). Violence risk assessment: Combining actuarial and clinical information to structure clinical judgements for the formulation and management of risk. *Journal of Psychiatric and Mental Health Nursing*, *9*(6), 649–57.

Fawcett, J., Scheftner, W.A., Fogg, L., Clark, D.C., Young, M.A., Hedeker, D. et al. (1987). Clinical predictors of suicide in patients with major affective disorders: A controlled prospective study. *American Journal of Psychiatry*, *144*, 35–40.

Freshwater, D. & Westwood, T. (2006). Risk, detention and evidence: Humanizing mental health reform. *Journal of Psychiatric and Mental Health Nursing*, *13*(3), 257–9.

Harrison, G., Gunnell, D., Glazebrook, C., Page, K. & Kwiecinski, R. (2001). Association between schizophrenia and social inequality at birth: Case-control study. *British Journal of Psychiatry, 179*, 346–50.

Harriss, L., Hawton, K. & Zahl, D. (2005). Value of measuring suicidal intent in the assessment of people attending hospital following self-poisoning or self-injury. *British Journal of Psychiatry, 186*, 66–8.

Hawton, K., Rodham, K., Evans, E. & Weatherall, R. (2002). Deliberate self harm in adolescents: Self report survey in schools in England. *British Medical Journal, 325*(7374), 1207–11.

Klonsky, E.D., Kotov, R., Bakst, S., Rabinowitz, J. & Bromet, E.J. (2012). Hopelessness as a predictor of attempted suicide among first admission patients with psychosis: A 10-year cohort study. *Suicide and Life Threatening Behavior, 42*(1), 1–10.

Kreitman, N. & Foster, J. (1992). The construction and selection of predictive scales, with special reference to parasuicide. *British Journal of Psychiatry, 159*, 185–92.

Lee, H.C., Lin, H.C., Liu, T.C. & Lin, S.Y. (2008). Contact of mental and nonmental health care providers prior to suicide in Taiwan: A population-based study. *Canadian Journal of Psychiatry, 53*(6), 377–83.

Linehan, M.M. (1993). *Cognitive Behavioral Treatment of Borderline Personality Disorder*. New York: Guilford Press.

Luoma, J.B., Martin, C.E. & Pearson, J.L. (2002). Contact with mental health and primary care providers before suicide: A review of the evidence. *American Journal of Psychiatry, 159*(6), 909–16.

Lupton, D. (1999). *Risk*. London: Routledge.

MacLeod, A.K., Pankhania, B., Lee, M. & Mitchell, D. (1997). Brief communication: Parasuicide, depression, and the anticipation of positive and negative future experiences. *Psychological Medicine, 27*, 973–7.

Meltzer, H., Lader, D., Corbin, T., Singleton, N., Jenkins, R. & Brugha, T. (2002). *Non-Fatal Suicidal Behaviour among Adults aged 16 to 74 in Great Britain*. London: The Stationery Office.

Morgan, A. & Felton, A. (2013). From constructive engagement to coerced recovery. In S. Coles, S. Keenan & B. Diamond (Eds.), *Madness Contested: Power and practice* (pp. 56–73). Ross-on-Wye: PCCS Books.

Morgan, J. (2007). *'Giving Up the Culture of Blame': Risk assessment and risk management in psychiatric practice*. London: Royal College of Psychiatrists.

Office of National Statistics. (2013). *Statistical Bulletin: Suicides in the United Kingdom, 2011*. Retrieved 25 November 2013 from http://www.ons.gov.uk/ons/rel/subnational-health4/suicides-in-the-united-kingdom/2011/stb-suicide-bulletin.html

Ovenstone, I.M.K. & Kreitman, N. (1974). Two syndromes of suicide. *British Journal of Psychiatry, 124,* 336–45.

Pilgrim, D. & Tomasini, F. (2013). Mental disorder and the socio-ethical challenge of reasonableness. In S. Coles, S. Keenan & B. Diamond (Eds.), *Madness Contested: Power and practice* (pp. 74–89). Ross-on-Wye: PCCS Books.

Read, J., van Os, J., Morrison, A.P. & Ross, C.A. (2005). Childhood trauma, psychosis and schizophrenia: A literature review with theoretical and clinical implications. *Acta Psychiatrica Scandinavica, 112,* 330–50.

Reznek, L. (1997). *Evil or Ill? Justifying the insanity defence.* London: Routledge.

Ritsher, J.E.B., Warner, V., Johnson, J.G. & Dohrenwend, B.P. (2001). Intergenerational longitudinal study of social class and depression: A test of social causation and social selection models. *British Journal of Psychiatry, 178*(Suppl. 40), s84–90.

Royal College of Psychiatrists (RCP). (2008). *Rethinking Risk to Others in Mental Health Services: Final report of Scoping Group.* London: Royal College of Psychiatrists.

Schotte, D.E. & Clum, G.A. (1987). Problem-solving skills in suicidal psychiatric patients. *Journal of Consulting and Clinical Psychology, 55,* 49–54.

Shaw, J., Hunt, I.M., Flynn, S., Meehan, J., Robinson, J., Bickley, H. et al. (2006). Rates of mental disorder in people convicted of homicide: National clinical survey. *British Journal of Psychiatry, 188,* 143–7.

Shaw-Welch, S. (2001). A review of the literature on the epidemiology of parasuicide in the general population. *Psychiatric Services, 52,* 368–75.

Silver, E., Felson, R.B. & Vaneseltine, M. (2008). The relationship between mental health problems and violence among criminal offenders. *Criminal Justice and Behavior, 35*(4), 405–26.

Swinson, N.A., Ashim, B., Windfuhr, K.L., Kapur, N.N., Appleby, L. & Shaw, J. (2007). National confidential inquiry into suicide and homicide by people with mental illness: New directions. *Psychiatric Bulletin, 31,* 161–3.

Szmukler, G. (2000). Homicide inquiries: What sense do they make? *Psychiatric Bulletin, 24,* 6–10.

Thornicroft, G. (2006). *Shunned: Discrimination against people with mental illness.* New York: Oxford University Press.

Vinkers, D.J., De Beurs, E., Barendregt, M., Rinne, T. & Hoeck, H.W. (2012). Proportion of crimes attributable to mental disorders in the Netherlands population. *World Psychiatry, 11*(2), 134.

Witteman, C. (2004). Violent figures, risky stories. *Advances in Psychiatric Treatment, 10,* 275–6.

part II: action plans, policies and sharp edges

'we must turn these actions green by the end of the week'

'By the end of the meeting, we must have blitzed this action plan,' said Desmond, the Head of Service, to the gathering of lead clinicians and senior managers sitting around a rectangular table. In front of each of us lay a 12-page document detailing 21 discrete directives that our inpatient psychiatric unit were required to implement. Each action was colour-coded: red indicating 'no progress'; amber, 'partial achievement'; and green, 'fully achieved'. Given the service leader's stated aspiration for the meeting, the absence of green evoked feelings of foreboding among those present.

The action plan under scrutiny originated from a post-incident review (PIR) completed 18 months earlier in response to a serious incident where a 26-year-old female patient had absconded from one of the inpatient wards and jumped from a nearby bridge, sustaining serious injuries to her legs and pelvis. A comprehensive investigation had ensued, culminating in a 150-page report retrospectively analysing the untoward event and generating seven recommendations that had translated into the 21 actions that now lay before us.

The young woman who had jumped from the bridge reported an extended history of deliberate self-harm and had acquired the diagnostic label of 'emotionally unstable personality disorder', an enduring mental health problem characterised by relationship instability, expectations of abandonment by others, rapidly fluctuating feelings and habitual self-injurious behaviour. While residing on the ward, the nursing staff had found her challenging behaviour difficult to manage and, as is often the case for patients with this presentation (one the psychiatrists usually perceive to be 'not a proper mental illness'), mental health professionals had fundamentally disagreed about what would represent an appropriate service response.

The directives contained within the action plan addressed a variety of areas, including the proper procedures to be followed (for example, the level of nursing observation that vulnerable, self-harming patients should receive) and the kind of therapeutic interventions that should be offered. As always, each action on the plan included the name of a specific manager or senior clinician tasked with the overall responsibility for its successful implementation. Despite the action plan being 18 months old, I had not previously been alerted to its contents. While Desmond introduced the primary purpose of the meeting, each participant (with various degrees of trepidation) thumbed the action plan to discover the designated, as-yet-incomplete actions for which they were about to be held accountable.

Past experience had taught me that the directives within action plans can usually be categorised as either tokenistic or unrealistic, neither of which enhances the quality of service. The two items carrying my name provided an example of each. Firstly, I was responsible for ensuring that 'a clinical psychologist is available to offer advice and guidance about the management of patients with personality disorder'. At face value, this recommendation could be construed as helpful: people with complex and enduring problems can benefit from an individually tailored management plan that strives to set limits of behaviour alongside ensuring opportunities for therapeutic progress, all informed by the individual's unique psychological presentation. But there already existed a small clinical psychology resource dedicated to the inpatient unit that was 'available' to discuss the complex array of difficulties displayed by people with personality disorders. The challenge for the service was how to ensure that the ward nurses and doctors perceived it as sufficiently relevant to their practice to motivate them to use it. As such, this stated action simply reiterated the status quo.

The second action with my name on fell into the 'wholly unrealistic' category. It required that 'All patients with personality disorder should be offered one-to-one psychological therapy.' With only one clinical psychologist responsible for four inpatient wards, it would not have been feasible to provide the appropriate (and lengthy) therapies to just a fraction of this group of patients, and a sheer impossibility to offer it to them all.

'Over the last couple of years, the Trust has experienced an unusually high number of serious untoward incidents,' said Desmond, 'and it is imperative that we provide evidence that we are taking all reasonable steps to improve the situation. Ensuring action plans are completed is one important part of this process.'

Desmond proceeded to read out each action in turn and ask the named, responsible individual for evidence of progress. Confronted with this demand, my management colleagues muddled through, creatively highlighting snippets of evidence that might be considered relevant to each action, apparently sufficient for Desmond to feel justified in converting a few reds to greens.

'OK Gary, what about this clinical psychologist being available to offer advice?'

'For the last five years we have had a dedicated clinical psychologist for the inpatient unit, but the problem is ....'

'Excellent,' said Desmond. 'So we can clearly turn that one green. And where are we up to with offering all our personality-disordered patients psychological therapy?'

'I'm afraid that's unrealistic given that we have only one psychologist on the unit, and no one else qualified to deliver such therapies.'

'Oh,' said Desmond, as he sighed.

'Maybe we could acknowledge our lack of resources to deliver this action and put together a proposal to develop further psychological therapy skills within the staff on the inpatient wards?' I said, in an attempt to be constructive.

'Yes, we could discuss that further in due course. But I require something on this action plan to show the Trust executives when I meet with them on Friday. Do any patients on the unit receive therapy?'

'Yes, one or two,' I said.

'Great, we can document that some patients are already in receipt of psychological therapy and turn that one amber.'

By the end of the meeting, the action-plan landscape had been transformed from all red to predominantly green with the occasional amber speck. Desmond smiled and thanked us all for our hard work; he now had something to appease his managers in three days' time, to show them that as a service we were striving to reduce the risk of serious incidents in the future. But what had a three-hour meeting of the most senior (and highly paid) clinicians and managers actually achieved? No improvement in the effectiveness of the service offered to patients, nor any reduction in the future probability of risky events. Its sole achievement was to eliminate the potential to be criticised for not completing relevant action plans should there be another serious incident, and subsequent investigation, in the future.

the peril of nameplates

Upon returning to my office at the administrative base in the Psychology Department, I recognised that something within the physical environment had changed. After a few seconds of deliberation, it registered with me that the recently installed nameplates on the office doors had all vanished. The 12- by 3-inch white plastic brackets, emblazoned with prominent black lettering, and fitted only a fortnight before, had been removed.

'What's happened to the nameplates on the doors?' I asked the administration manager.

'Oh yes, we had to scrap them; the Facilities Department informed us that they infringed health and safety requirements.'

'How come? Were they made from Semtex?'

'No,' said the manager, smiling at my sarcasm. 'They apparently had sharp edges.'

'So what was their concern?'

'The guy that rang me said there was a risk that we might cut ourselves while slotting them in and out.'

'So when will the replacements be here?'

'He didn't know precisely; he said they'd have to purchase some more, and it could take between 6 to 12 weeks.'

At this point in time, the offices in the Psychology Department were no longer used for clinical interventions, these instead being delivered in the community mental health centres, GP practices, inpatient units and people's own homes. So the nameplate removals could not be justified on the basis of reducing access to means of self-harm for services users with suicidal inclinations. I was left reflecting on how taxpayers would react to the knowledge that public funds were being frittered away on the paternalistic mission to eliminate even the most tenuous of risks from the work environment. In the twenty-first century National Health Service, individual responsibility is an alien concept.

beware the unconventional policy!

My role of senior clinician incorporated some line-management responsibilities for more junior colleagues. It was, therefore, imperative to remain acquainted with the relevant Trust policies around issues such as staff recruitment, managing staff misconduct or poor practice, and responding to complaints from service users.

One morning, I was required to attend a training event to become acquainted with some recent changes made to the 'Health and Safety Policy', a 30-page document detailing the specific responsibilities of all employees (from the Chief Executive and senior and middle managers, through to each individual practitioner) in the multifaceted endeavour to prevent harm to any person (staff member, service user or contractor) involved within the organisation. At the end of the presentation, as we were gathering our belongings in readiness to leave, a senior representative from our 'Clinical Governance' department requested that we remain seated for a further 20 minutes so as to hear about a new policy that had recently been developed.

The title of this new piece of guidance was 'How to construct a formal guidance document'. It took a few seconds to register that the reason we were obliged to delay our lunch was to listen to a bureaucrat describe a policy about writing policies! The presenter distributed the 12-page document and proceeded, via PowerPoint slides, to enlighten us about the appropriate sequence of subheadings to use when constructing a new policy document. The building blocks for an optimal policy were, apparently, the sequence of: introduction, purpose, definitions, duties (of the board, chief executive, executive directors, heads of service, managers and staff), policy overview diagram, policy detail, monitoring and review arrangements, feedback, consultation, approval and ratification, training requirements, resource issues, and reference documents.

The participants endured the session in silence until, towards the end, one of the more candid nurse managers raised his hand to ask a question.

'Can I just check I understand this right; all of us are expected to use these subheadings when involved in constructing a new policy?'

'Yes,' said the trainer. 'By using this structure it will ensure that the policy covers all the relevant areas and will aid its utility when it is drawn upon by services.'

'Why then have you not used your subheadings when writing this policy?'

The flustered presenter muttered something about this new directive constituting a special case, but was visibly crumbling under the weight of the hypocrisy accusation.

Subsequently, as we ate our belated lunch, the policy about how to write policies not adhering to its own directives evoked much merriment. The farcical event seemed to encapsulate the bureaucratic culture of the modern National Health Service.

will someone please make a decision!

Sixty-two-year-old Jimmy had endured an eventful and challenging life. Complications at birth resulted in some mild learning difficulties that impaired both his school performance and his relationships with peers. His father left the home before Jimmy's sixth birthday at which point his mother, tasked with the sole responsibility for Jimmy and his two older siblings, struggled to cope and began to drink excessively. Subsequently, Jimmy suffered physical, sexual and emotional abuse from his mother, as well as victimisation from a succession of his mother's alcohol-abusing partners. At infant school his poor academic performance and disruptive behaviour resulted in his expulsion from the mainstream and his attendance at a special school for the remainder of his education. While at special school, he formed an affirming relationship with a male teacher who (unlike any other adult throughout his childhood) invested time in Jimmy and taught him a range of practical skills, including carpentry at which he excelled. Regrettably, upon leaving special school at the age of 16, Jimmy drifted into gang activity and, at the age of 19, received a three-year prison sentence for his involvement in a violent assault on another young man.

Jimmy's first contact with psychiatric services occurred at 22 years of age, precipitated by his repeated self-harming behaviour and threats of suicide. Around this time he reported hearing voices, the content of which was always derogatory, typically echoing his mother's words in telling him he was a 'useless piece of shit'. He also expressed ideas of persecution, that others were intent on inflicting harm – at least some of which may have had validity given his earlier gang involvement. Throughout the subsequent 40 years, Jimmy underwent recurrent admissions to psychiatric hospitals, typically following self-mutilation or high-profile suicidal behaviour – threatening to leap from a motorway bridge for example – throughout which his personal life remained chaotic, characterised by interpersonal conflict with neighbours and family members. Predictably, Jimmy had acquired a variety of diagnostic labels from his contacts with psychiatric services, including paranoid schizophrenia, borderline personality disorder, depression, antisocial personality disorder, adjustment reaction and paranoid personality disorder. Many psychiatric professionals who had worked with Jimmy now viewed him as a difficult, 'heart-sink' patient.

From a psychological perspective, Jimmy's lifelong emotional and behavioural difficulties could be understood by his past experiences of abuse and disempowerment leading him to harbour themes of worthlessness, of having no control over his life and a fundamental mistrust of other people. Based on these themes, Jimmy's range of challenging and problematic behaviours could be construed as his desperate attempts to extract affirmation and concern from others, to regain a sense of control and to feel part of something worthwhile.

Discussion with Jimmy of this simplified framework for understanding his ongoing problems demonstrated that it made sense to him – an imperative if this outline was to be helpful.

Promoting a more positive self-view, by means of engagement in valued roles, was identified as an important way forward. However, Jimmy's suspiciousness around the motives of others; his reputation within psychiatric services of being a 'difficult' patient; and his previous criminal record – all collectively presented challenges in accessing a position where he could routinely carry out some worthwhile activity. Jimmy had often been encouraged to pursue voluntary work during his four decades of contact with psychiatric services but, unfortunately, no consistent participation had been achieved. Sometimes, a combination of reticence about meeting new people and his chaotic lifestyle conspired to thwart his initial attendance at the work placement. On the occasions he had attended, interpersonal conflict with peers had led to his premature withdrawal or expulsion. Sometimes, the work opportunity was rescinded before it began when his Criminal Records Bureau check (a legal requirement prior to employment in roles where children or other vulnerable people were involved) highlighted his historical conviction for violence.

On this occasion, however, both Jimmy and I were more optimistic. Not only did he seem to recognise the central importance of a valued role in promoting positive self-esteem, but also we both believed we had identified an optimal niche. During his many inpatient admissions Jimmy had forged a positive relationship with one of the caretakers, a man of similar age to Jimmy whose responsibilities included the completion of minor repairs within the hospital buildings. The caretaker expressed enthusiasm about Jimmy assisting him with specific tasks, and Jimmy, for the first time, displayed eagerness at the prospect of feeling helpful in relation to a man he respected, as well as demonstrating his own proficiency in practical joinery. The three of us agreed that it would be sensible to introduce the voluntary work gradually, so two mornings a week seemed an appropriate starting point. All we now required was the permission of the relevant manager to proceed.

I arranged to meet the matron who had managerial responsibility for most of the hospital areas where we envisaged Jimmy's work would take place. I explained the background and the voluntary work proposal.

'Sounds like a great idea,' she said, 'and you have my full support. You will, however, need to run it past my senior manager.'

Several phone calls and multiple emails later, I finally managed to meet the assistant director with responsibility for the residential units, whereupon I repeated the outline of Jimmy's history and the rationale underpinning the plan.

'I'm impressed by your commitment and creativity,' she said. 'Given his mental instability we will require a written reference from a senior clinician who knows Jimmy well, stating that he is safe to perform the work proposed. Also, you will need to seek guidance from our HR (human resources) department regarding where we stand with the CRB check.'

Dutifully, I committed the background and rationale to paper, arguing that there were clear grounds for positive risk taking, stating that, although no initiative of this kind could ever be free of any risk, the anticipated risks were minor while the potential gains were substantial. I sent copies of my testimony to the matron, the senior manager and the HR department. Two weeks later I had not received a response from HR, so I rang them and, after some toing-and-froing between several personnel officers, I was advised to consult with one of their senior people. A further four-week delay ensued before such a meeting could go ahead.

'Someone with a conviction for grievous bodily harm on his CRB would usually be excluded from working voluntarily in our organisation,' said the personnel officer.

'It was over 40 years ago, when he was a teenager,' I said, 'and there have been no further convictions.'

'But we must take into consideration the fact that he will be working among vulnerable people.'

'He'll be with the caretaker repairing furniture and sweeping floors. And the plan is to start with just two mornings per week and see how it goes.'

The personnel officer stroked his chin as he perused the paperwork. 'To deviate from our usual practice we will need written authority from the relevant manager to reassure us that this patient no longer poses a threat.'

'I've already provided this information, explaining why I think Jimmy should be offered this opportunity,' I said.

'But we will need something from the manager in charge of the area where he will be working, taking responsibility should there be an untoward incident.'

So I contacted the assistant director again, relaying this request.

'I'm not in a position to give this reassurance, as I don't know the patient,' she said. 'Ask the matron; she'll be much more conversant with his behaviour than me.'

So I spoke with the matron again.

'I don't feel able to go out on a limb without the written authority of my senior manager or HR,' she said.

After six months pursuing formal permission to proceed with the voluntary work placement, during which time Jimmy understandably experienced increasing frustration and disillusionment, we were ultimately obliged to abandon the project. Despite all parties apparently conceiving the initiative as sensible and worthwhile, in the risk-averse culture of the National Health Service no manager felt able to formally support it.

7

---

there is no hope for
the brain-diseased

part I: pessimism and low expectation

Hope is an essential component of mental wellbeing. The enduring belief that enjoyable experiences – achievements, pleasurable events, closeness to others – lie ahead motivates us all to persist with efforts to overcome life's challenges. Without hope, existence is rendered futile.

This section will explore how hope acts as both a protective factor against suicide and an engine to persist with efforts to recover from mental health problems. The ways by which traditional psychiatry quashes hope will be discussed, and a normalising approach to psychotic experiences will be outlined as a more optimistic (and valid) framework for understanding psychotic disorders. The second half of the chapter will detail illustrative examples of how the medically dominated psychiatric system unwittingly stifles the hopes and aspirations of the very people it is commissioned to serve.

hopelessness and suicidal behaviour

People who suffer mental health problems display a significantly elevated risk of suicidal behaviour. For example, it has been estimated that those suffering with depression are four times more likely to commit suicide as compared to the general population, the risk rising to 20-fold greater when the disorder is severe (Bostwick & Pankratz, 2000). Similarly, it is recognised that psychosis sufferers constitute another high-risk group, the typical emergence of the disorder in young adulthood impeding educational and vocational ambitions (Birchwood et al., 2000).

It has long been known that individuals prone to suicidal behaviour differ from other, less-risky people in the way they construe the future (Baumeister, 1990). Negative thinking about the future has chiefly been conceptualised as hopelessness, a construct typically measured by responses to 20 true-or-false items on a questionnaire referred to as the Beck Hopelessness Scale (BHS) (Beck et al., 1974). The BHS, one of the most widely used questionnaires in routine psychiatric practice, requires the respondent to endorse or reject statements such as 'The future looks dark to me' and 'In the future, I expect to succeed in what concerns me most'. Based on these responses, a level of hopelessness is calculated.

As mentioned in Chapter 6, research has established hopelessness as a central contributor to suicidal behaviour. Thus, there is evidence that hopelessness predicts repetition of sub-lethal self-harm (Petrie, Chamberlain & Clarke, 1988), completed suicide (Beck, Brown & Steer, 1989; Fawcett et al., 1990), and attempted suicide in people following a first episode of psychosis (Klonsky et al., 2012). Furthermore, hopelessness appears to mediate the relationship between depression and suicidal intent (Wetzel et al., 1980; Salter & Platt, 1990).

For some time, the essence of hopelessness remained unclear; did it represent a perception of multiple adverse events in the future, an expectation that nothing positive lay ahead, or a combination of these strands? Clarification was achieved by MacLeod and his collaborators (MacLeod, Rose & Williams, 1993; MacLeod et al., 1997, 2005) who conducted a series of experiments in which hopeless people were asked to generate as many occurrences in the future (both trivial and important) that they were either looking forward to or not looking forward to. Whereas they found that they were less able to think of future positive events when compared to controls, there was no appreciable difference in their fluency for events they were not looking forward to. The overarching conclusion from this series of studies was that a lack of positive anticipation underpinned hopelessness rather than an over-prediction of negative events.

Consideration of the links between hopelessness and suicide, along with the identification of a lack of positive anticipation as the crucial element of hopelessness, lead to the conclusion that perceiving a future with some enjoyable experiences will immunise against suicidal inclinations.

hope and recovery from mental health problems

People who present to psychiatric services are typically experiencing unprecedented levels of both distress and disruption to their lives. A primary challenge for professionals is to promote (or maintain) hope that a rewarding and worthwhile life is attainable beyond the mental disorder. The imperative of instilling hope has been documented in both best-practice guidance and relevant research aiming to underscore the elements of an effective mental health service.

The central importance of mental health services adopting a recovery approach, so as to enable service users to achieve worthwhile lives, has been emphasised by both policymakers and clinical researchers (see Chapter 5, pp. 85–6). The government's vision for mental health, outlined in its *New Horizons* document, includes the aspiration that: 'In a high quality service, the principles of recovery and the concepts of hope, self-determination and opportunity that come under its umbrella, underpin the practice of all those offering care and treatment' (DH, 2009, p. 24).

The concept of a 'recovery approach' to mental health is a nebulous one, its foundation comprising a range of key values and principles. Consequently, a number of academic researchers have attempted to define the essential features of a recovery-orientated service. A systematic review of all such studies by Leamy et al. (2011) concluded that there were five overarching recovery processes, one of which they described as 'hope and optimism about the future' (p. 445).

But what practical steps do mental health services need to implement so as to demonstrate they are moving towards more recovery-orientated provision? Shepherd, Boardman and Burns (2010) provided guidance in the form of a methodology by which services could meet 10 'organisational challenges' so as to propel them in the direction of optimal, routine practices that were consistent with a recovery ideology. With regards to organisational challenge 1, 'Changing the nature of day-to-day interactions and the quality of experience', the authors recommend that every staff encounter should aim to 'increase opportunities for life "beyond illness" and validate hope' (Shepherd et al., 2010, p. 8). In a similar vein, organisational challenge 4 ('Creating the culture') requires that a fully recovery-orientated service should promote 'an environment of hope and optimism that recognises the uniqueness and strengths of each individual' (Shepherd et al., 2010, p. 11).

biological psychiatry and the crushing of hope

Given the central importance of sustaining hope to immunise against suicide and to inject momentum into service users' recovery journeys, one might reasonably expect modern psychiatric services to instinctively project optimism towards the people they serve. Lamentably, this is not the case. Although many clinicians, from a range of professional disciplines, do routinely offer encouragement and hope, the biological paradigm for making sense of mental health problems that dominates contemporary psychiatric practice inherently stymies the aspirations of many service users. How can an individual retain a positive anticipation of a rewarding future in the context of habitual interactions with powerful 'experts', the majority of whom believe that their distress and impaired functioning is primarily the result of a brain disease?

There has been formal recognition of the existing disparity between policy aspirations for recovery-orientated services and actual clinical practice. For example, Repper and Perkins (2012) highlighted how current services, in keeping with a biological ('illness like any other') approach to mental health problems, continue to display a narrow focus on the treatment of symptoms rather than offering more holistic support for recovery. This disparity between aspiration and clinical reality should come as no surprise; within any mental health service, a biological skew and a recovery orientation are incompatible constructs.

the service user perspective
The most potent evidence that traditional psychiatric services habitually emit unhelpful pessimistic messages derives from the testimonies of the service users themselves. A study by Lester, Tritter and Sorohan (2005), involving focus groups composed of both patients and professional staff, reported a mismatch between service users and service providers in the way that mental health problems were perceived. While the patients emphasised the importance of optimism and hope, the professionals were inclined to view severe mental illness as a lifelong condition, drawing parallels with medical disorders such as diabetes and heart disease.

The importance of the interaction between service users and mental health professionals in promoting (or crushing) hope has been highlighted by Hobbs and Baker (2012). In-depth interviews with people experiencing mental health problems, and who were receiving ongoing input from psychiatric services, suggested a vital role for staff–patient relationships in maintaining the level of hope required for successful recovery. The cherished beliefs clinicians hold about the primary cause of mental disorders will inevitably shape the level of optimism conveyed within these relationships.

A similar study by Kartalova-O'Doherty and Doherty (2010), involving intensive interviews with 15 long-term service users, revealed that staff assumptions of illness chronicity typically translated into their telling their charges that they would require professional support and medication for the rest of their lives. Such bleak prophecies were, according to the service users, instrumental in their decisions to 'give up' and accept an enduring role as a mental patient.

Further evidence that traditional psychiatry inflicts a continuous stream of pessimistic messages upon many people with mental health problems derives from an American survey of over 1,000 service users (Faught, 2012). When the full range of psychiatric disorders was included, almost 40 per cent of service users stated they had received a 'hopeless message' regarding the potential for recovery. For those service users given the diagnostic labels of 'schizophrenia' or 'bipolar disorder', the percentage hearing hopeless messages was even greater.

Exploration of the source of these hopeless messages led to the shameful discovery that the mental health care provider was the most culpable, indicted by 76 per cent of those hearing that recovery was unlikely; even the media, with its penchant for sensationalism, accounted for only 62 per cent. Seventy-six per cent were told by a mental health professional that they would have to take medication for the rest of their lives; 64 per cent were never told during their contact with mental health services that recovery was possible; while 41 per cent were informed that recovery was impossible. Furthermore, almost half were specifically told that they could not achieve a personally valued goal.

Many personal stories, typically compiled by mental health advocacy organisations, powerfully convey the essence of the hope-crushing messages delivered by psychiatric services. One service user succinctly recounted: 'I was assured I was going to be mentally ill for the rest of my days, as if I was being given a life sentence with no possibility of parole' (Mad in America, 2012).

As well as unhelpful, such negative messages about the likelihood of recovery are invalid. Even when medical conceptualisations of 'schizophrenia' are considered, along with narrow, symptom-reduction definitions of recovery, the expectation is that around 80 per cent of sufferers will, in time, achieve some significant improvement (Royal College of Psychiatrists, 2014). In the Faught (2012) survey (discussed above) almost two-thirds of the respondents who had been told that recovery was impossible did, at the time of the study, rate themselves as 'recovered'. It is therefore reasonable to conclude that there is a blatant disparity between the recovery predictions habitually emanating from psychiatric professionals and the actual outcomes for service users.

the benefits of normalising unusual experiences

The hope-quashing consequences of applying a biological illness framework to people with mental health problems is closely associated with its 'all-or-nothing', categorical approach to human distress. By definition, if a person is diagnosed with a mental illness the immediate implication is that this person is abnormal, distinguishable from the vast majority of his or her peer group on the basis of a biochemical imbalance or brain aberration. Given this alleged internal defect, one that is outside the realm of the individual's control, it is not surprising that many people so labelled feel hopeless about their chances of attaining a worthwhile life in the future.

An alternative means of making sense of mental health problems adopts what is often referred to as a 'continuum' approach (for example, Johns & van Os, 2001). Unlike the categorical system of biological psychiatry, which assumes a clear dividing line between the ill and the normal, continuum approaches assert that experiences such as voice hearing and paranoia are present, to various degrees, across the whole population. Within this framework, the only difference between a disturbed psychosis sufferer and someone functioning adequately is a quantitative one – the former experiencing a relatively common phenomenon but to an extreme degree. There is plentiful evidence to support this normalising approach to mental health.

psychotic symptoms in the general population

A number of studies have explored the degree to which experiences such as voice hearing and delusional beliefs (symptoms viewed as important to inform the diagnosis of schizophrenia) are present in the general population.

With regards to hearing voices that are undetectable to other people in the vicinity, Tien (1991) estimated that around 3 million people in the United Kingdom, 5 per cent of the population, hear voices at any given time. Many of these voice hearers will not have had, nor need, contact with psychiatric services. The lifetime prevalence of hallucinatory experiences was found to be somewhere between 8 to 15 per cent. Johns et al. (2002) conducted a community survey of 8,000 people in England and Wales and found that 4 per cent endorsed a question about the experience of hallucinations in the previous year, the rate being notably higher in Afro-Caribbean than white or Asian samples.

A recent review by Beavan, Read and Cartwright (2011), incorporating 17 surveys from nine countries, found wide variation in reported voice-hearing prevalence from study to study, with a mid-range figure of around 13 per cent.

The conclusion that voice hearing is prevalent in a significant minority of the general population is unsurprising when one considers the life events that predispose to such experiences. These contributory factors include childhood abuse (Romme & Escher, 1989; Read et al., 2005), bereavement (Reese, 1971; Grimsby, 1993), sleep deprivation (Oswald, 1974), solitary confinement (Grassian, 1983), and cannabis misuse (Johns, 2001).

Delusions (unusual beliefs that endure despite an apparent lack of evidence to support them) appear to have an even greater prevalence in the general population than voice hearing. Verdoux et al. (1998) reported that up to 70 per cent of the general population endorse beliefs that could be construed as delusional. Similarly, a study by Peters et al. (2004), involving the completion of a 'delusion inventory' (a questionnaire incorporating 21 items asking about a range of delusional beliefs typically considered during the psychiatric diagnostic process), found that at least some of the items were endorsed by the vast majority of a non-psychiatric population. Importantly, the scores on the questionnaire followed a normal distribution curve (with the majority registering intermediate scores, and relatively few at the low and high extremes) in much the same way as constructs such as intelligence. Furthermore, the scores from people without a psychiatric history overlapped significantly with those diagnosed with a psychotic disorder who were, at the time of the study, inpatients on an acute psychiatric unit. These two findings (a normal distribution and overlap between non-clinical and clinical populations) demonstrate the legitimacy of adopting a continuum approach to delusional beliefs.

A Dutch study by van Os et al. (2000) provided additional evidence in support of the assertion that the same kind of delusional beliefs are prevalent in both healthy and psychiatric populations. Their survey of over 7,000 people established that 12 per cent of the general population held delusional beliefs. Follow-up interviews with psychiatrists judged only a quarter of these deluded people to have 'true' delusions, the unusual beliefs of the remainder being evaluated as having no clinical relevance. One can therefore conclude that there are many more well-functioning people in the community harbouring unusual beliefs than there are deluded service users in the psychiatric system.

A number of widespread environmental factors have been shown to contribute to the emergence of unusual beliefs, thereby explaining their high prevalence in the general population. The life experiences that make delusional beliefs more likely include victimisation and discrimination (Mirowsky & Ross, 1983; Bentall & Fernyhough, 2008), overly critical, domineering parents (Rankin et al., 2005), and low socio-economic, socially challenging backgrounds (Mirowsky & Ross, 1983; Cromby & Harper, 2009).

implications for services

The awareness that voice hearing and unusual beliefs are commonplace within the general population, and that the frequency and prominence of these phenomena lie on a continuum, is often enabling for people grappling with mental health problems. In contrast to the categorical 'ill' or 'not ill' approach deployed by traditional psychiatry, a normalising frame encourages service users to construe their experiences as an extension of what many people display – both psychiatric patients and those functioning well in the community. Thus, differences between individuals are viewed as being ones of degree rather than the products of a relatively static and internal pathology, thereby promoting optimism that desired change is within reach.

A prominent example of the enabling qualities of a normalising paradigm is provided by the Hearing Voices Movement (see Longden, Corstens and Dillon, 2013, for an overview). Underpinned by the pioneering work of Romme and Escher (1993, 2000), the Hearing Voices Movement counteracts the stigmatising effects of the conventional illness model by embracing and celebrating the diversity of the voice-hearing population. Within this thriving network, incorporating people from all sections of society, voice hearing is construed as a normal human experience that can be understood in the context of each person's unique life experiences. The approach has expanded in popularity, among both voice hearers and professional staff, and Hearing Voices networks have now been established in 21 countries, including the UK and the USA.

A more structured way of utilising a normalising approach to mental health problems involves explaining a person's unusual experiences as an extension of common thinking errors that we all make at one time or another. For example, an extended version of the universal self-serving bias (whereby we attribute positive outcomes to ourselves and negative ones to the behaviour of others) may underpin paranoia (Kaney & Bentall, 1989; Fear, Sharp & Healy, 1996). Similarly, a tendency to prematurely jump to conclusions on the basis of limited evidence may also contribute to persecutory beliefs (Bentall, Kinderman & Kaney, 1994; Bentall et al., 2001; Bentall, 2004). Distressing voice-hearing experiences may result from a misattribution of our inner speech (the ubiquitous process of covert self-talk) to an external source (Bentall, 2004) along with the subsequent deployment of counterproductive strategies to try to control them (Morrison, 2001).

Further non-medical conceptualisations of unusual experiences have emphasised the role of aversive external factors in the emergence of paranoia. According to Cromby and Harper (2013), the mistrust and hostility characteristic of the paranoid state are fuelled by 'toxic social and material circumstances' (p. 29).

Explaining unusual experiences as understandable products of everyday thinking errors and life events is not without pitfalls; the perception of harbouring cognitive deficits or of ongoing confinement in an impoverished environment each risks conveying a negative message about the prospect for change. Nevertheless, by offering both psychological and social support, along with the highlighting of the common prevalence of voice hearing and delusional beliefs among the general population, much of the pessimism intrinsic to biomedical approaches can be avoided.

references

Baumeister, R.F. (1990). Suicide as escape from self. *Psychological Review*, *97*, 90–113.

Beavan, V., Read, J. & Cartwright, C. (2011). The prevalence of voice-hearers in the general population: A literature review. *Journal of Mental Health*, *20*(3), 281–92.

Beck, A.T., Brown, G. & Steer, R.A. (1989). Prediction of eventual suicide in psychiatric inpatients by clinical ratings of hopelessness. *Journal of Consulting and Clinical Psychology*, *57*, 309–10.

Beck, A.T., Weissman, A., Lester, D. & Trexler, L. (1974). The measurement of pessimism: The Hopelessness Scale. *Journal of Consulting and Clinical Psychology*, *42*(6), 861–5.

Bentall, R.P. (2004). Abandoning the concept of schizophrenia: The cognitive psychology of hallucinations and delusions. In J. Read, L.R. Mosher & R.P. Bentall (Eds.), *Models of Madness: Psychological, social and biological approaches to schizophrenia* (pp. 195–208). London: Routledge.

Bentall, R.P., Corcoran, R., Howard, R., Blackwood, R. & Kinderman, P. (2001). Persecutory delusions: A review and theoretical integration. *Clinical Psychology Review*, *21*, 1143–92.

Bentall, R.P. & Fernyhough, C. (2008). Social predictors of psychotic experiences: Specificity and psychological mechanisms. *Schizophrenia Bulletin*, *34*, 1012–20.

Bentall, R.P., Kinderman, P. & Kaney, S. (1994). The self, attributional processes and abnormal beliefs. Towards a model of persecutory delusions. *Behaviour Research and Therapy*, *32*, 331–41.

Birchwood, M., Iqbal, Z., Chadwick, P. & Trower, P. (2000). Cognitive approach to depression and suicidal thinking in psychosis. *British Journal of Psychiatry*, *177*, 522–8.

Bostwick, J.M. & Pankratz, V.S. (2000). Affective disorders and suicide risk: A reexamination. *American Journal of Psychiatry*, *157*, 1925–32.

Cromby, J. & Harper, D. (2009). Paranoia: A social account. *Theory and Psychology*, *19*(3), 335–61.

Cromby, J. & Harper, D. (2013). Paranoia: Contested and contextualised. In S. Coles, S. Keenan & B. Diamond (Eds.), *Madness Contested: Power and practice* (pp. 56–73). Ross-on-Wye: PCCS Books.

Department of Health (DH). (2009). *New Horizons: A shared vision for mental health*. London: Mental Health Division, Department of Health.

Faught, S. (2012). Where do messages of hopelessness in mental health care come from? Retrieved 10 May 2014 from http://www.madinamerica.com/2012/12/messages-of-hopelessness/

Fawcett, J., Scheftner, W.A., Fogg, L., Clark, D.C., Young, M.A, Hedeker, D. et al. (1990). Time-related predictors of suicide in major affective disorder. *American Journal of Psychiatry*, *147*(9), 1189–94.

Fear, C., Sharp, H. & Healy, D. (1996). Cognitive processes in delusional disorders. *British Journal of Psychiatry*, *168*, 61–7.

Grassian, G. (1983). Psychopathological effects of solitary confinement. *American Journal of Psychiatry*, *140*, 1450–4.

Grimsby, A. (1993). Bereavement among elderly people: Grief reactions, post-bereavement hallucinations and quality of life. *Acta Psychiatrica Scandinavica*, *87*, 72–80.

Hobbs, M. & Baker, M. (2012). Hope for recovery – how clinicians may facilitate this in their work. *Journal of Mental Health*, *21*(2), 144–53. DOI:10.3109/09638237.2011.648345.

Johns, A. (2001). Psychiatric effects of cannabis. *British Journal of Psychiatry*, *178*, 116–22.

Johns, L.C., Nazroo, J.Y., Bebbington, P. & Kuipers, E. (2002). Occurrence of hallucinatory experiences in a community sample and ethnic variations. *British Journal of Psychiatry*, *180*, 174–8.

Johns, L.C. & van Os, J. (2001). The continuity of psychotic experiences in the general population. *Clinical Psychology Review*, *21*(8), 1125–41.

Kaney, S. & Bentall, R.P. (1989). Persecutory delusions and attributional style. *British Journal of Medical Psychology*, *62*, 191–8.

Kartalova-O'Doherty, Y. & Doherty, D.T. (2010). Recovering from recurrent mental health problems: Giving up and fighting to get better. *International Journal of Mental Health Nursing*, *19*(1), 3–15.

Klonsky, E.D., Kotov, R., Bakst, S., Rabinowitz, J. & Bromet, E.J. (2012). Hopelessness as a predictor of attempted suicide among first admission patients with psychosis: A 10-year cohort study. *Suicide & Life Threatening Behavior*, *42*(1), 1–10.

Leamy, M., Bird, V., Le Boutillier, C., Williams, J., & Slade, M. (2011). Conceptual framework for personal recovery in mental health: Systematic review and narrative synthesis. *British Journal of Psychiatry*, *199*, 445–52.

Lester, H., Tritter, J.Q. & Sorohan, H. (2005). Patients' and health professionals' views on primary care for people with serious mental illness: Focus group study. *British Medical Journal*, *330*(7500), 1122.

Longden, E., Corstens, D. & Dillon, J. (2013). Recovery, discovery and revolution: The work of Intervoice and the Hearing Voices Movement. In S. Coles, S. Keenan & B. Diamond (Eds.), *Madness Contested: Power and practice* (pp. 161–80). Ross-on-Wye: PCCS Books.

MacLeod, A.K., Pankhania, B., Lee, M. & Mitchell, D. (1997). Brief communication: Parasuicide, depression and the anticipation of positive and negative future experiences. *Psychological Medicine*, *27*, 973–7.

MacLeod, A.K., Rose, G.S. & Williams, J.M.G. (1993). Components of hopelessness about the future in parasuicide. *Cognitive Therapy and Research*, *17*(5), 441–55.

MacLeod, A.K., Tata, P., Tyrer, P., Schmidt, U., Davidson, K. & Thompson, S. (2005). Hopelessness and positive and negative future thinking in parasuicide. *British Journal of Clinical Psychology*, *44*(4), 495–504.

Mad in America. (2012). *Psychiatry Almost Drove Me Crazy.* Retrieved 23 December 2013 from http://www.madinamerica.com/2012/12/psychiatry-almost-drove-me-crazy/

Mirowsky, J. & Ross, C.E. (1983). Paranoia and the structure of powerlessness. *American Sociological Review*, *48*, 228–39.

Morrison, A. (2001). The interpretation of intrusions in psychosis. *Behavioural and Cognitive Psychotherapy*, *29*, 257–76.

Oswald, I. (1974). *Sleep* (3rd ed.). Harmondsworth: Penguin Books.

Peters, E., Joseph, F., Day, S. & Garety, P. (2004). Measuring delusional ideation: The 21-item Peters et al. Delusions Inventory (PDI). *Schizophrenia Bulletin*, *30*, 1005–22.

Petrie, K., Chamberlain, K. & Clarke, D. (1988). Psychological predictors of future suicidal behaviour in hospitalized suicide attempters. *British Journal of Clinical Psychology*, *27*, 247–58.

Rankin, P., Bentall, R.P., Hill, J. & Kinderman, P. (2005). Perceived relationships with parents and paranoid delusions: Comparisons of currently ill, remitted and normal participants. *Psychopathology*, *38*, 16–25.

Read, J., van Os, J., Morrison, A.P. & Ross, C.A. (2005). Childhood trauma, psychosis and schizophrenia: A literature review with theoretical and clinical implications. *Acta Psychiatrica Scandinavica, 112*, 330–50.

Reese, W.D. (1971). The hallucinations of widowhood. *British Medical Journal, 4*(5778), 37–41.

Repper, J. & Perkins, R. (2012). Recovery: A journey of discovery for individuals and services. In P. Phillips, T. Sandford & C. Johnston (Eds.), *Working in Mental Health: Practice and policy in a changing environment* (pp. 71–80). Oxford: Routledge.

Romme, M. & Escher, A. (1989). Hearing voices. *Schizophrenia Bulletin, 15*, 209–16.

Romme, M. & Escher, S. (1993). *Accepting Voices*. London: Mind.

Romme, M. & Escher, S. (2000). *Making Sense of Voices*. London: Mind.

Royal College of Psychiatrists (RCP). (2014). *Schizophrenia*. Retrieved 9 January 2014 from http://www.rcpsych.ac.uk/healthadvice/problemsdisorders/schizophrenia.aspx

Salter, D. & Platt, S. (1990). Suicidal intent, hopelessness and depression in a parasuicide population: The influence of social desirability and elapsed time. *British Journal of Clinical Psychology, 29*, 361–71.

Shepherd, G., Boardman, J. & Burns, M. (2010). *Implementing Recovery: A methodology for organisational change*. London: Sainsbury Centre for Mental Health.

Tien, A.Y. (1991). Distributions of hallucinations in the population. *Social Psychiatry and Psychiatric Epidemiology, 26*, 287–92.

van Os, J., Hanssen, M., Bijl, R.V. & Ravelli, A. (2000). Strauss (1969) revisited: A psychosis continuum in the general population? *Schizophrenia Research, 45*, 11–20.

Verdoux, H., Maurice-Tison, S., Gay, B., van Os, J., Salamon, R. & Bourgeois, M.L. (1998). A survey of delusional ideation in primary-care patients. *Psychological Medicine, 28*, 127–34.

Wetzel, R.D., Margulies, T., Davis, R. & Karam, E. (1980). Hopelessness, depression, and suicide intent. *Journal of Clinical Psychiatry, 41*, 159–60.

part II: we shouldn't expect too much

but they're not 'recovery ready'

In keeping with the rhetoric of contemporary mental health provision, in 2012 our NHS Trust was striving to develop services characterised by a 'recovery orientation'. The essence of this worthy aim was to ensure that all aspects of our psychiatric service, including each interaction between clinician and service user, achieved consistency with the values and principles of a recovery ideology. The central strands of this sought-after philosophy included the promotion of social networks, a positive self-view, active engagement in life, and hope.

A collective of like-minded professionals and service users, referred to as the 'recovery collaborative', had been tasked with the formidable challenge of encouraging recovery practices across the organisation. One element of this mission involved the introduction of a new assessment tool, the Recovery Star (Mental Health Providers Forum & Triangle Consulting, 2011). The Recovery Star incorporates 10 dimensions (for example, social networks, living skills, and trust and hope) considered vital for the achievement of a rewarding and worthwhile life. The service user 'owns' the assessment and, in discussion with key professional staff, determines the priority personal goals. For each dimension there is a visually appealing ladder that the service user completes to monitor incremental progress. At the time, the lengthy core assessment employed across the secondary mental health services involved the laborious completion of a multiple-page 'needs assessment' – a time-consuming task typically undertaken exclusively by the professional, the outcome of which realising only modest influence on the service user's goals and planned interventions.

As a member of the recovery collaborative, I participated in a sequence of initiatives aimed at encouraging more recovery-orientated practices, including the adoption of the Recovery Star to replace the existing bureaucratic and service-driven assessment framework. An essential step towards the introduction of any new venture like the Recovery Star involved what organisations verbosely refer to as 'consultation with relevant stakeholders' – in essence, asking those likely to be affected by the proposed change what they think. The views of three groups of people were sought: the service users; the service managers; and the clinical staff, mainly comprising psychiatric nurses, who would (if the initiative proceeded) support the service users to both complete the Recovery Star and track subsequent progress.

The service users who participated in the recovery collaborative expressed unbridled enthusiasm about the proposed new assessment. We decided, however, to sample a much wider range of service user opinion by delivering a presentation to the Trust's service user forum (an established Trust committee representing the interests of service users) and subsequently circulating the Recovery Star document and seeking feedback, from both individuals and the forum. The responses we received indicated widespread enthusiasm for the new assessment:

> I like the way the ladders show my progress; this would keep me going through the bad times.

> It's good that we can decide what's important to us and work on these areas first.

> It's all about me!

> This is the kind of stuff we should be talking about in my 6-monthly reviews.

> I had a go at filling it in and found that I am doing really well in a couple of the areas – Responsibilities and Addictions – so despite all the problems I'm having right now, I'm still good at something. Knowing this made me feel a bit better.

Although some minor concerns emerged (for example, about needing assistance to complete the assessment and worries about rating themselves accurately on each ladder) the thrust of service-user opinion demonstrated support and desire for the proposed change.

Subsequently, we delivered the same presentation to a group of middle and senior managers. They were broadly supportive of the proposal to introduce the Recovery Star, recognising that the implementation of a recovery-orientated initiative would gain approval from the Trust executives who would construe the change as an example of innovation. Our managers insisted that a comprehensive risk assessment would be required, alongside the Recovery Star, and expressed concerns that some of our partner organisations might not recognise the new assessment when patients were transferred into other services. But overall they agreed to facilitate the replacement of the existing core assessment framework with the Recovery Star, provided that the clinical staff were supportive of the change.

When we shared the details of the proposed new assessment with a group of clinical staff, in the first instance they responded positively. The striking visual representations of progress along each dimension appealed to them, as did the prospect of shrinking the administrative burden of multiple form-filling. Reasonably, they requested the opportunity to further discuss the Recovery Star with their peers via their monthly professional forums.

Four weeks later the Recovery Collaborative received a collective written response from the psychiatric nursing staff stating that, although they recognised that the Recovery Star could be helpful for working with some patients, they did not support its introduction as the core assessment for the community mental health teams. Their specific concerns that had informed this conclusion were as follows:

> Although we could see how the Recovery Star would be useful for some patients who are soon to be discharged, we felt that it would be much less appropriate for those in the acute phase of illness.
>
> It risks giving false hope to some of our patients – for example, those with chronic schizophrenia – who will, in all likelihood, never recover.
>
> The Recovery Star would be ideal for working with patients on standard CPA [those with less complex problems] but much less appropriate for those on enhanced CPA [those with complex and/ or high risk problems].
>
> It would be inappropriate for those patients with severe and enduring mental illness.
>
> Patients would have to reach the stage of being 'recovery-ready' before they could benefit from using the Recovery Star.

In addition to betraying the misconception that recovery from mental health problems is essentially about the elimination of symptoms (rather than the achievement of a worthwhile life irrespective of ongoing problems), the feedback from experienced and well-intentioned nursing colleagues starkly demonstrated the pervasive lack of positive expectations for the people they attempt to help. The language ('chronic schizophrenia' and 'severe and enduring'), terms that remain prevalent within contemporary psychiatric services, revealed underlying assumptions about the inevitability of unrelenting mental disorder consistent with assumed brain disease. Or, at best, patients had to achieve a state of being 'recovery-ready' (presumably via medical treatments to remedy chemical imbalances) as an essential prerequisite for the recovery journey.

This opposition thwarted the initiative to introduce the Recovery Star as the core assessment framework across the services. Instead the new assessment tool, much favoured by service users, was introduced in a piecemeal fashion, beginning with specific elements of the service where the staff were supportive of recovery principles. At the time of writing, two years on, the Recovery Star is only accessible to a small minority of service users within the Trust.

a life sentence at 21

The psychiatrist announced the verdict. Ryan's father flinched, and his mother, fumbling to retrieve a tissue from her handbag, began to sob. Ryan, the patient, stared straight ahead, his blank expression suggesting an internal struggle to understand the implications of the doctor's words.

Ryan's mental health problems had emerged two years earlier during his first year at university studying civil engineering. Following a weekend of heavy drinking, Ryan had expressed bizarre ideas that his student friends were involved in an elaborate plot to frame him for the murder of a teenager. (It later emerged that a 14-year-old in Ryan's class at school had suffered a fatal stabbing seven years earlier.) Ryan's suspiciousness had escalated into full blown paranoia, screaming threats at anyone who approached him. The police were called and admission to psychiatric hospital ensued under a section of the Mental Health Act. Ryan's inpatient stay spanned three months during which time he was deemed to have suffered a psychotic episode and initially prescribed haloperidol (one of the older, 'first-generation' types of antipsychotic medication). Once Ryan's level of agitation had waned, olanzapine (a 'second-generation' antipsychotic generally believed to evoke less disabling side effects) replaced haloperidol and was prescribed on an ongoing basis.

In the immediate aftermath of the psychotic episode, Ryan's mood dipped and he expressed pessimism about ever leading a normal life. He previously had ambitions of a career in civil engineering and would often tell his parents and friends that he would seriously consider emigrating to the USA or Australia if that would enhance the opportunity to earn his fortune. He sensed that his mental illness diagnosis, and the stigma surrounding it, would quash his chances of fulfilling these aspirations. Furthermore, his bizarre and abusive behaviour had scared off almost all his friends, as well as straining his three-year relationship with his partner.

Upon discharge from psychiatric hospital, Ryan was fortunate to receive support from a progressive 'early intervention' service – a relatively well-resourced multidisciplinary team whose practitioners carried smaller caseloads than their counterparts in the community mental health teams, and who deployed a normalising, continuum approach to the unusual experiences that biological psychiatrists would typically label as 'schizophrenia'. In addition to his olanzapine medication, Ryan received both psychological therapy (to help him manage his low mood and to make sense of his recent paranoia) and social support (encouraging engagement in community-based, age-relevant activities). During this period, Ryan spent time with other young people who had suffered psychotic episodes and benefited from hearing authentic recovery stories about the many people who had succeeded in achieving productive and rewarding lives. The team also encouraged Ryan to re-establish his friendship network and to liaise with the university about the prospect of continuing his academic studies.

After working with the early intervention service for 18 months, Ryan had discovered his previous ambitions and expressed optimism about his future. He had learned about the high prevalence of unusual beliefs in the general population and had realised that there were many other people, from all backgrounds, who had experienced similar ideas. As a result of the psychological therapy, he had assumed a relatively benign explanation for the emergence of his unusual experiences based on a combination of past experience (the murder of his schoolmate), sleep deprivation and substance misuse (the occasional smoking of cannabis). Moreover, his parents, who had described feeling 'devastated' in the immediate aftermath of their son's psychotic episode, were now more hopeful about what lay ahead. The frequency of Ryan's contact with his care co-ordinator (a social worker named Penny) was reduced to once per fortnight, and the university had agreed for him to return to his studies in three months' time.

But then came the multidisciplinary review meeting. In keeping with the statutory requirement to formally evaluate the appropriateness of the team's interventions at least every six months, all the professionals involved (psychiatrist, psychologist, social worker and support worker) met with Ryan and his parents to discuss progress and to plan for the future. Penny chaired the meeting and asked each participant to provide feedback on developments since the previous review. Ryan enthusiastically described his recent achievements in re-establishing friendships, routine involvement in leisure activities (including football and a weekly music group), learning strategies to manage his low mood, and his imminent return to his engineering studies. His parents expressed delight and admiration at the way their son had worked hard to get his life back on track, and were effusive in their compliments for the team members who had won Ryan's trust and enabled him to 'reconnect with life'. I, the psychologist, provided an outline of what Ryan had accomplished in therapy. Penny and the support worker provided further details of Ryan's constructive engagement in groups and community activities.

The psychiatrist had only recently been assigned to Ryan's case (following a service redesign) and, prior to the meeting, had not met Ryan or his parents. Up to this point, while we all enthused about the various aspects of Ryan's progress, the psychiatrist had sat reading the case notes, occasionally looking up to nod and smile, before returning his gaze to the folder resting on his knee. When Penny asked if he would like to share his own views on what he had heard, the psychiatrist looked directly at Ryan.

'It is pleasing to hear that the olanzapine is doing such a good job.'

Ryan glanced around the room, as if waiting for someone else to respond, but as he continued to be the focus of the psychiatrist's gaze, he realised the comment was addressed to him. 'I guess so.'

'Is there anything you would like to ask about your illness or the medication?' asked the psychiatrist.

Ryan shuffled in his chair, and looked towards his parents.

'Go on Ryan, ask him,' said his father. 'Me and your mum will leave the room if you wish.'

'No, it's OK,' said Ryan, and turned to the psychiatrist. 'Could I start to reduce the olanzapine?'

'It would not be wise to change the medication at this stage, given that you are now symptom-free. Maybe it's something we could look at in the future.'

'But I can't get an erection when I'm with my girlfriend, and it's really embarrassing. I've read that this is a common problem with this type of medication; I never used to have a problem in this department.'

The psychiatrist sighed. 'You have suffered a severe mental illness, and as we have now got it under control it would be foolish ....'

'But it's really bothering him,' said Ryan's father. 'It's shaking his confidence, as it would for any man of his age.'

The psychiatrist appeared irritated by this interruption. 'You have to accept that your son is suffering with a brain disease and, if he is to remain well, will have to take antipsychotic medication for the rest of his life.'

While Ryan's mother wept, Penny and I (trying to remain professional) emphasised that there was more than one way of making sense of psychotic experiences and there were no grounds for assuming it to be a life sentence. But the damage had already been done.

After the meeting, the exchange of views between the psychiatrist and me was considerably less diplomatic.

the man who talked to the trees

Between the ages of 16 and 28, several of Stuart's behaviours and interests corresponded to those of someone who could be described as a hippie. He maintained his hair at shoulder length, wore psychedelic-coloured shirts, and exhibited a penchant for sandals (if he felt obliged to wear anything on his feet at all). He adopted a vegetarian diet, participated in peaceful protest against wars and in support of animal welfare, and showed devotion to the music of Bob Dylan and Joan Baez. He regularly smoked a modest amount of cannabis and, on two occasions, experimented with LSD. An intelligent man, Stuart thought deeply about the pervasive problems in the world and read widely.

Stuart also harboured unusual beliefs. Since his teenage years he believed that all living things (plants and animals) were connected and habitually communicated with each other via a medium he referred to as the 'fourth dimension'. He openly disclosed to others how he would, on a daily basis, speak to the trees adjacent to his home and how they would respond to him in language only accessible to those, like himself, well-practised in the art of meditation.

Despite these eccentricities, Stuart functioned well throughout his teenage years and early adulthood. He benefited from a circle of close friends, comprising a mix of those with similar views to his own and those with more conventional ideologies, the latter of whom affectionately referred to their friend as 'hippie Stuart'. Neither did his unusual beliefs prevent him from earning a comfortable living; he held down a full-time job in a shoe factory and by the age of 28 had earned promotion to the role of production manager.

Unfortunately, at the age of 32, Stuart's life spun out of control. In the aftermath of his discovery that his long-term partner had been covertly involved with another man, his escalating cannabis use triggered a disturbing psychotic episode characterised by paranoid ideas that his neighbours were plotting to kill him. One evening, in a distraught and highly agitated state, he pounded on all the doors of the houses in his street and threatened to kill them if they did not cease their campaign to destroy him. Stuart's disturbed behaviour led to his admission to a psychiatric inpatient facility where he acquired the diagnosis of 'schizophrenia', and antipsychotic medication was initiated.

By the time of his referral to the Psychology Department, Stuart had received psychiatric services for seven years comprising six-monthly appointments with his psychiatrist (primarily to oversee progress and monitor the medication) and fortnightly supportive visits from a community psychiatric nurse. The expressed reason for seeking psychology input at this stage made reference to his low mood and withdrawal from life. During our initial psychology sessions, Stuart articulately described a solitary existence, living alone and only leaving his flat to buy groceries from the shop at the end of his street or to fulfil what he regarded as his monthly obligation to see an elderly aunt. He had quit his job and, apart from the occasional visit from an ex-colleague, all links with his friends had been severed.

Despite being virtually symptom-free for five years, further exploration revealed that the nub of Stuart's reticence to re-engage with life involved a fear of experiencing of another psychotic episode. The paranoid feelings in the prelude to his hospital admission had been terrifying, and Stuart described 'playing safe' so as to avoid a reoccurrence. On the occasions when he detected a hint of unusual experience (suspecting the trees were communicating with him, for example) his level of anxiety would rise; when these concerns were relayed to the psychiatric professionals, the response invariably involved an increase in his antipsychotic medication so as to dampen what the service described as these 'low-level symptoms of psychotic illness'.

When we explored the events leading up to his psychotic episode, Stuart recognised that his excessive cannabis use (smoking 20 joints each day at its peak) represented, by far, the most potent contributory factor to the emergence of his paranoia. Stuart had remained abstinent from cannabis throughout his contact with psychiatric services, and emphatically denied any possibility of returning to this habit. He understood that, while he remained cannabis-free, the likelihood of a further psychotic episode was remote. Yet any hint of unusual experiences continued to scare him.

The essence of Stuart's dilemma emerged during a psychology session when we were reviewing his progress in some tasks we had negotiated at our previous appointment. As a first step to promoting re-engagement with life, Stuart had agreed to catch a bus into a local town to buy his groceries (rather than using the shop at the end of his street).

'How did you get on with the bus into town?' I asked.

'I did it but it freaked me out,' said Stuart, going on to explain that the peak of his anxiety arose on the bus while passing through a wooded area.

'Tell me what you were experiencing at this point, and the thoughts running through your mind.'

'I could hear the trees whispering to me, via the fourth dimension. And I thought a couple of people sitting in front of me were thinking I was some kind of psycho-freak.'

'I can imagine that must have felt really uncomfortable, having thoughts that people were thinking badly of you while in a public place. With regards to your sense that the trees were whispering to you, how did that experience compare to those you have described having in the years prior to your psychotic episode?'

Stuart pondered for a few moments. 'The same in some ways, but different in others; the sounds from the trees were pretty much the same as they'd always been, but the whole experience felt very different this time – it was much more scary.'

'On this occasion it seems your experience of the trees triggered thoughts that others would view you as a "psycho-freak". What thoughts did you have on all those occasions in your early 20s when you sensed the trees were talking to you?'

'I didn't think much about it; I just felt good that I had a special gift of being able to get close to nature.'

We went on to further demonstrate how his interpretations of his tree-talking experience ('People will think I'm a psycho-freak' versus 'I have a special gift') would substantially determine his emotional reaction (scared versus privileged).

In subsequent psychology sessions I encouraged Stuart to re-evaluate his current negative interpretation of his lifelong unusual experiences. We also constructed a timeline of the relationship between his level of unusual experience and his corresponding degree of functioning, a graph that starkly demonstrated that Stuart performed best (socially and vocationally) with a moderate level of unusual experiences and much poorer at the other extremes (the full-blown psychotic episode and no unusual experiences at all). But despite these efforts, his negative view of his unusual experiences proved unshakeable. When we reflected on the likely reasons for this fixed position, Stuart highlighted the determining factor:

'I now know that I have a mental illness.'

As far as I am aware, Stuart continues to tolerate an impoverished life, avoiding further unusual experiences via a combination of antipsychotic medication and self-imposed isolation from other people (and trees).

reference

Mental Health Providers Forum & Triangle Consulting. (2011). *Mental Health Recovery Star*. London: Mental Health Providers Forum. Retrieved 14 October 2014 from http://www.centreformentalhealth.org.uk/pdfs/ Recovery_star_user_guide.pdf

8

an unholy alliance

part I: psychiatry and the pharmaceutical industry

The symbiotic relationship between biological psychiatry and the multinational drug companies represents one of the most pernicious collusions in peacetime history. Following the discovery of chlorpromazine (the precursor of a group of medications later referred to as antipsychotics) in the 1950s, the synergistic manoeuvres of psychiatry and the pharmaceutical industry succeeded in creating a fantastical world of ubiquitous mental illness and chemical cures.

This chapter will provide an overview of their dubious practices, including disease mongering, exaggerated claims regarding the efficacy of drugs, indiscriminate prescribing and blatant malpractices. A more realistic, evidence-based appraisal of the benefits and drawbacks of psychiatric drugs will be presented. The discussion will primarily focus on antipsychotics, with secondary reference to antidepressants, although the arguments are, to varying degrees, applicable to all types of medication dedicated to the treatment of mental health problems. Part II will provide an illustration of how some drug-company-sponsored practices play out in contemporary psychiatric services.

disease mongering

Biological psychiatrists assume that mental health problems can be dissected into discrete, meaningful categories in the same way as physical diseases. Since the start of the twentieth century, psychiatrists have striven to identify explicit diagnostic criteria that would indicate the presence of a distinct mental illness, a defining moment in this endeavour being the publication in 1980 of the third edition of a comprehensive classification system, referred to as the *Diagnostic and Statistical Manual*, or *DSM-III* for short (American Psychiatric Association [APA], 1980). Despite being rendered meaningless on account of their poor validity and reliability (Bentall, 2009), several more revisions of the *DSM* have ensued and they continue to be influential across research, clinical and political arenas.

The veneer of scientific respectability allows these arbitrary classification systems to be applied in ways that mislead, one example being the inflated estimates of the prevalence of mental illnesses. A diagnostic interview deploying *DSM-III-R* criteria with a community sample in the USA led to the assertion that almost 50 per cent of the population had been afflicted with at least one mental disorder during their lives, inspiring the authors to advocate for more proactive psychiatric outreach methods (Kessler et al., 1994). A more recent study, involving 17 countries and using *DSM-IV* criteria, estimated the lifetime prevalence for one or more disorders to range from 12 per cent in Nigeria to 47 per cent in the USA (Kessler et al., 2007).

The more blatant practices of drug companies in sponsoring diseases so as to expand profitable markets have been described by Moynihan and his colleagues (Moynihan, 1998; Moynihan et al., 2002). For example, once the antidepressant Paxil had been approved by the regulatory authorities for the treatment of severe shyness ('social phobia') the drug company's advertising posters incorporated the prompt, 'Imagine being allergic to people'. When the same drug won formal approval in the USA for the treatment of excessive worrying ('generalised anxiety disorder') in 2001, GlaxoSmithKline set in motion a huge public relations operation to raise the profile of the 'disease' (Koerner, 2002). Such publicity campaigns typically involve the co-ordinated efforts of drug companies, 'independent experts' (in the form of psychiatrists) and consumer groups.

excessive prescribing

Alongside the disease-mongering process identifying ever more people as mentally ill, there have been inflated claims regarding the efficacy of the medication used to treat them. At its most extreme, some commentators construed the introduction of antipsychotic medication as representing unbridled progress, instrumental in establishing the discipline of psychiatry as a bona fide medical specialism (for example, Shorter, 1997). Although over recent years the growing evidence to the contrary has tempered the wilder claims of efficacy, the antipsychotics continue to represent the foundation of treatment for people diagnosed as suffering with schizophrenia. At the time of writing, the website of the Royal College of Psychiatrists (RCP) in the United Kingdom states that around 80 per cent of patients will benefit from antipsychotic medication (RCP, 2014a). Furthermore, clinical practice guidelines from around the world universally recommend the prescribing of antipsychotics as the initial treatment for a first episode of psychosis (Gaebel et al., 2005).

With regards to antidepressants, the current view of the RCP is that three months of treatment will render between 50 to 60 per cent of depressed patients as 'much improved' (RCP, 2014b). The implicit assumption that antidepressant medication is the only feasible treatment for depression is indicated by the following statement on the informational website of the American Psychiatric Association (APA): 'If a patient feels little or no improvement after several weeks, his or her psychiatrist will alter the dose of the medication or will add or substitute another antidepressant' (APA, 2014).

The last 20 years has witnessed an explosion in the consumption of antipsychotics and antidepressants, partly caused by the routine prescribing for problems outside of their primary remit (Ornstein, Stuart & Jenkins, 2000; Verdoux, Tournier & Bégaud, 2010). Ilyas and Moncrieff (2012) calculated that antipsychotic prescribing in England had increased by 5.1 per cent each year between 1998 and 2010, during which time it overtook antidepressants as the most expensive type of psychiatric medication. In the USA 3.1 million people were prescribed antipsychotics in 2011 at a cost of $18.2 billion, the newer ('atypical') drugs, aripiprazole and quetiapine, achieving the status of leading sellers (IMS Institute for Healthcare Informatics, 2012).

As for antidepressants, between 1998 and 2010, prescribing in England accelerated at a rate of 10 per cent each year (Ilyas & Moncrieff, 2012) and in 2011 alone almost 47 million prescriptions were issued, a rise of 9 per cent on the previous year (Health and Social Care Information Centre, 2012a). In the USA in 2011 a staggering 18.5 million people (around one in 14 of the population aged 14 years and older) were ingesting antidepressant drugs at a cost of $11 billion (IMS Institute for Healthcare Informatics, 2012).

Marketing strategies by the pharmaceutical industry to extend the range of target mental disorders for their drugs have been a resounding success, with receptive doctors routinely prescribing one type of antidepressant medication (the selective serotonin reuptake inhibitors or SSRIs) for a range of anxiety disorders in addition to depression (Moret, Isaac & Briley, 2009), as well as for people without a diagnosable mental disorder (Olfson & Marcus, 2009). Consonant with the 'illness like any other' mythology, there is also evidence that antidepressants and antipsychotics are being prescribed over longer periods of time (Osborn et al., 2007; Moore et al., 2009).

Even vulnerable old people and children have failed to elude the tentacles of the marketing campaign to promote the antipsychotics. In 2011 around 25 per cent of all dementia sufferers in the United Kingdom (180,000 people) were prescribed antipsychotics (Health and Social Care Information Centre, 2012b), a figure that is likely to underestimate the practice of tranquillising confused and agitated older people, as it only includes primary care settings. Children and adolescents displaying behavioural problems or mood instability have also been increasingly prescribed antipsychotics, particularly in the USA (Olfson et al., 2006; Verdoux et al., 2010).

deception and dishonesty

The unholy alliance of drug companies and biological psychiatrists has spawned malpractices of a more blatant kind that range from the highly selective and self-serving sharing of information, to bribery and stark criminality.

hiding unfavourable data

Science and commercialism present a dodgy combination where truth and profit may be mutually exclusive. In order to earn money for the pharmaceutical industry, each drug requires scientific evidence to support its effectiveness and to demonstrate superiority over its competitors. Such a terrain is fertile soil for bias and distortion.

Goldacre (2012) highlights the disturbing fact that 90 per cent of all published clinical trials, purporting to apply the objectivity of science to investigate the effectiveness of drugs, are sponsored by the pharmaceutical companies. The ensuing flaws in the way this research is conducted, and the results communicated, have been comprehensively addressed by Goldacre. The sources of the self-serving distortions include: the use of trivial or meaningless outcome measures that are of little consequence to the patient, such as demonstrating that a drug reduces the symptoms of schizophrenia by 10 per cent (Gilbody, Wahlbeck & Adams, 2002); failing to report the intended outcomes because they show the drug in a poor light and, instead, trawling the data for some other measure that might show an improvement; comparing the new drug against a weak alternative (for example, one associated with many side effects) so as to ensure it appears superior (Safer, 2002); excluding the results of those patients who dropped out of the study, who may have done so owing to lack of improvement or marked side effects; and (perhaps the most sinister of all) the failure to publish results that suggest the new drug may be ineffective or damaging.

The publication bias is particularly troublesome. Goldacre (2012) asserts that only half of all drug trials are reported in the academic journals and those that generate unfavourable results for the new drug are twice as likely to go missing as compared to those that report positive ones. The work of Bourgeois, Murthy and Mandl (2010) provides further evidence for this reporting bias; analysis of over 500 drug trials, including some involving antidepressants, found that more than 85 per cent of the drug-company-sponsored studies reported positive results for the new drug, as compared to 50 per cent that were government funded.

It is not only the drug companies and biological psychiatry researchers who are culpable for 'research misconduct on a grand, international scale' (Goldacre, 2012, p. 80). Responsibility also lies with: ethics committees (for allowing researchers with a history of hiding data to conduct more trials); university administrators (for formally agreeing to contracts that permit the drug companies to control the data); academic journals (for continuing to publish trials whose protocols, and the researchers' plans and intentions, had not previously been registered); regulators (for their poor systems and obstructiveness when approached for information); and governments (for failure to implement laws compelling companies to publish data). Goldacre cogently argues that this catalogue of failure conceals the true risks and benefits of new drugs and, in so doing, inflicts unnecessary suffering (even death) on patients.

bribing stakeholders
Over recent years the corruption and malpractices of the pharmaceutical industry, together with their biological psychiatry associates, have evoked censure, prosecution and media headlines. One high-profile case involved the drug company GlaxoSmithKline, who in 2012 admitted to 'corporate misconduct' and were fined $3 billion (£1.9 billion) (Neville, 2012). The company was guilty of energetically promoting the antidepressant drug, Paxil, for use with children and teenagers despite the licence restricting its use to adults. Regardless of three trials that had failed to show that Paxil achieved any benefits for children, Glaxo published a report entitled 'Positioning Paxil in the adolescent depression market – getting a head start'. During the court hearing the prosecution also claimed that the company paid $275,000 to a doctor as an inducement to promote another antidepressant, Wellbutrin, for unapproved uses (including weight gain and sexual dysfunction) on his popular US radio show. Furthermore, so-called 'independent' psychiatrists were induced to endorse the drug company's products by means of lavish financial

rewards and hospitality. In the words of the US attorney involved in the case, 'The sales force bribed physicians to prescribe GSK products using every imaginable form of high-priced entertainment, from Hawaiian vacations and paying doctors millions of dollars to go on speaking tours, to tickets to Madonna concerts' (Neville, 2012).

Another glaring example of malpractice relates to American psychiatrist Dr Joseph Biederman, who has energetically promoted antipsychotic prescribing for the treatment of mood disorders in children. In 2008, under investigation by Republican Senator Charles Grassley, Biederman belatedly admitted that between 2000 and 2007 he had earned at least $1.6 million in consulting fees from drug companies, most of which he had failed to disclose to university officials, thereby violating federal and university rules designed to avoid conflicts of interest (Harris & Carey, 2008).

Drug-company inducements to promote their products are ubiquitous across psychiatric services. Although typically not reaching the threshold for blatant malpractice, they shape the behaviour of psychiatric professionals and their patients in favour of their own brand of medications. The pharmaceutical industry spends twice as much on marketing its products as it does on research and development (Goldacre, 2012), and much of this pot is deployed to fund drug representatives to routinely visit doctors and persuade them that their products are the best. Often young and physically attractive, they swoop into health centres and GP practices, bestowing gifts, partisan information, as well as food and refreshments for clinical meetings. Despite doctors often claiming (somewhat naïvely) that these drug representatives do not sway their clinical judgement, the evidence to the contrary is undeniable: physicians who have regular contact with them are significantly more likely to prescribe their products (Spurling et al., 2010).

The tentacles of the pharmaceutical industry's marketing enterprise extend beyond the workplaces of medical and psychiatric professionals, with concerted efforts to directly influence the ultimate consumers – that is, the people with mental health problems. Patient groups, who offer support and information to fellow sufferers of a particular disorder, often receive a significant amount of their funding from drug companies, and there is evidence that this sponsorship impacts on their behaviour and priorities (see Goldacre, 2012, pp. 266–71).

Direct-to-consumer advertising (speaking directly to the general public through media advertisements) has, predictably, been a prized objective of the pharmaceutical industry. Prohibited since the 1940s, it re-emerged in the USA and New Zealand 40 years later. There is convincing evidence both that speaking directly to the public in this way increases patients' requests for the advertised drug and that doctors commonly acquiesce to such requests (Gilbody, Wilson & Watt, 2005; Kravitz et al., 2005). Converting people to patients (disease mongering) seems an important element of this type of marketing (Iizuka, 2004).

The effectiveness of the crudest type of direct persuasion, paying patients to take drugs, has recently been researched. Priebe et al. (2013) reported that a £15 incentive for each attendance at the depot clinic (the place where long-acting antipsychotics are injected into the patients' buttocks) promoted a modest increase in compliance. This additional adherence with medication achieved no improvement in clinical symptoms nor did it reduce the number of admissions to hospital. Refreshingly, it seems that clinical teams recognised the ethical issues associated with paying patients to take toxic medication; only 184 of the 540 teams approached consented to participate. Two authors in the study formally disclosed that they had received payment from drug companies during the study.

do antipsychotics work?

Anyone who has worked in psychiatric services will recognise how rare it is to discover a patient with a diagnosis of 'schizophrenia' (or other psychotic disorder) who has not been prescribed antipsychotic medication. But does their effectiveness justify this ubiquitous use?

With regards to psychosis, mainstream psychiatry routinely claims that antipsychotic medication benefits service users in two broad areas. Firstly, in the treatment of an acute psychotic episode, when the sufferer is plagued with some combination of hallucinations (usually voice hearing), delusions and jumbled thoughts; in this instance, the expressed purpose of the medication is to reduce or eliminate these distressing symptoms. Secondly, as a 'maintenance' intervention for patients who have previously experienced one or more psychotic episodes but who now display few, if any, symptoms; in this instance, the expressed purpose of the medication is to prevent further psychotic episodes (a 'relapse'). A concise review of the empirical evidence evaluating the effectiveness of antipsychotics in each of these areas will now be provided (see Moncrieff, 2013, for a more detailed discussion).

acute psychotic episode

There have been surprisingly few controlled studies of antipsychotic effectiveness in dampening the symptoms of an acute episode. The research that has been conducted suggests that antipsychotics are modestly superior to: a placebo (an inert tablet) (NIMH Psychopharmacology Service Center Collaborative Study Group, 1964; Johnstone et al., 1988), barbiturates (Casey et al., 1960), lithium (a 'mood stabiliser' mainly used for the treatment of bipolar disorder) (Johnstone et al., 1988), and psychotherapy (May, 1968). With regards to the comparison with lithium, a contrasting result was reported by Braden et al. (1982) who could find no superiority for chlorpromazine in reducing psychotic symptoms.

However, it is the direct comparisons with general sedation that cast doubt on psychiatry's ubiquitous assumptions that antipsychotics constitute a distinctively effective treatment for psychotic symptoms. Wolkowitz and Pickar (1991) reviewed all the well-designed studies testing the relative efficacy of antipsychotics and benzodiazepines, a class of drugs (of which Valium is the most well known) that reduce arousal and promote calmness or sleep. Three studies found benzodiazepines to be superior, two found in favour of antipsychotics, and three further studies could not distinguish between them. Given the research to date, it is reasonable to conclude that a drug's success in reducing psychotic symptoms may chiefly reflect a broad tranquillising effect rather than any specific antipsychotic action.

Although typically awarded a low profile in standard psychiatric textbooks, it is important to highlight that around 40 per cent of people who experience distressing psychotic symptoms can recover without antipsychotic medication (Bola & Mosher, 2002; Bola et al., 2006).

preventing psychotic relapse

Initial inspection of the available research suggests that ongoing use of antipsychotics may successfully reduce the likelihood of further psychotic episodes. A comprehensive review of 65 studies calculated that 64 per cent of patients withdrawn from antipsychotics met symptomatic criteria for relapse within one year as compared to only 27 per cent who continued taking the medication (Leucht et al., 2012a, 2012b), although only 26 per cent and 10 per cent respectively were admitted to hospital, suggesting the use of a low threshold for concluding 'relapse'. The same research team investigated the value of maintenance antipsychotic medication with people who had suffered their first episode of psychosis;

they reported similar advantages for the medicated group (Leucht et al., 2012b).

The negative effects of withdrawal from antipsychotics can, however, be tempered by active medication management of early signs of deterioration. For example, intermittent antipsychotic use in response to an initial increase in symptoms substantially eroded the advantage shown by the continuous antipsychotic group (Gaebel et al., 2002). The approach adopted by Carpenter et al. (1999) achieved a more striking outcome in demonstrating that brief periods of diazepam (Valium) prescribing in response to early signs of relapse matched the effectiveness of continuous antipsychotics. Overall, it is reasonable to conclude from these studies that around 30 to 40 per cent of psychosis sufferers can withdraw from antipsychotics without relapsing in the subsequent 12 months.

discontinuation effects

All research studies into antipsychotic effectiveness, with regards to both acute episodes and preventing relapse, exhibit at least some of the flaws highlighted by Goldacre (discussed above). However, the fundamental weakness in all these empirical investigations – the one which casts doubt over the conclusions drawn – is the potential for any benefits attributed to antipsychotic medication to derive primarily from discontinuation effects.

Over the last 50 years, psychosis sufferers who are not taking antipsychotic medication represent an almost extinct category of people. As such, all studies focusing on the efficacy of antipsychotics have essentially compared the consequences of ongoing antipsychotics with those of their withdrawal. The so-called placebo group, many of whom may have been long-term users of antipsychotics, have typically endured an abrupt cessation of their medication.

The deleterious effects, independent of any 'illness', of withdrawing from antipsychotics have long been recognised (Lacoursiere, 1976), common reactions including sleep disturbance, agitation and anxiety. Such experiences risk being misconstrued as a relapse of the psychotic illness, particularly when symptom-rating scales are used as an outcome measure, a common practice in research of this type. The fact that most 'relapses' cluster in the period immediately after antipsychotic withdrawal also supports the premise that many of these deteriorations represent a discontinuation effect (Baldessarini et al., 1995).

The human body displays a remarkable knack of reacting to outside interference with compensatory reactions aimed at restoring the status quo, a process referred to as homeostasis. Antipsychotic medications block brain receptor sites for neurotransmitters (chemical messengers), particularly those for dopamine, and the body responds by striving to enhance the sensitivity of these impeded receptors. Once the blockade is removed (withdrawal of the antipsychotic) there is a risk of 'supersensitivity' to psychosis (Chouinard & Jones, 1980) involving the appearance of paranoia and hostility that were not present prior to the start of drug treatment. A literature review of studies addressing the 'supersensitivity' effect concluded that 'psychosis may be a feature of drug withdrawal rather than the re-emergence of the illness' (Moncrieff, 2006, p. 3). Clozapine, an atypical antipsychotic medication widely prescribed for 'treatment-resistant' schizophrenia, seemed particularly prone to evoking such withdrawal effects, with weaker evidence that they might also occur with other antipsychotics.

atypical antipsychotics

The indecent haste and dubious research practices that characterised the introduction of atypical antipsychotics into the psychiatric market in the 1990s provides a microcosm of all that is wrong with the drug-company–psychiatry alliance. With growing awareness of the limitations and disturbing side effects of the first-generation antipsychotics, the atypicals were touted as a miracle cure that would revolutionise psychiatric practice; predictably, it turned out to be another false dawn.

Clozapine, the first atypical antipsychotic, fell out of favour in the mid-1970s following a report of it causing a profound suppression of the white blood cells (agranulocytosis) that had killed nine patients in Finland (Idänpään-Heikkilä et al., 1975, cited in Moncrieff, 2013). Clozapine re-emerged in the 1980s, followed by the trumpeting of other atypicals (risperidone, olanzapine, quetiapine, amisulpride, aripiprazole), and by the turn of the century they achieved formal recognition as the optimal first-line treatment of schizophrenia (National Institute for Health and Care Excellence, 2002).

The rush to demonstrate efficacy of the atypical antipsychotics in the 1990s encouraged drug trials that displayed a rancid combination of poor science and dishonesty. Examples of the former included: lax inclusion criteria, huge drop-out rates, poor-quality comparators and distorted reporting (see Moncrieff, 2013, pp. 107–11 for a comprehensive review). Furthermore, as the hastily assembled patients for the trials were predominantly long-term users of antipsychotics, the results would have been distorted by marked discontinuation effects in favour of the new atypical antipsychotics. As for blatant dishonesty, two psychiatrists (Richard Borison and Bruce Diamond) earned millions of dollars from the drug trials and were subsequently imprisoned for defrauding their employer (Whitaker, 2002). The prosecutors described how they had swindled their university out of more than $10 million and had disregarded patient safety in their quest to get results (Meyer, 1997).

Even with the sloppy and unethical research practices, the results of the early studies suggested that the atypical antipsychotics achieved only modest benefits for patients. A recent review of the literature, incorporating 32 clinical trials, has questioned whether any improvement attributable to these drugs is of a sufficient magnitude to significantly improve patients' lives (Khin et al., 2012). A similar review raised the possibility of a publication bias (only publicising studies that portray the new drug in a favourable light) and concluded that 'There is much room for more efficacious compounds' (Leucht et al., 2009, p. 429). Hardly the miracle cure as originally claimed.

do antidepressants work?

Despite the ubiquity of antidepressant medication in Western societies, recent research has suggested that any benefits associated with their use can predominantly be attributed to a placebo effect – that is, the changes achieved by the recipients' positive expectations of taking a drug when in reality, unknown to them, the drug is devoid of any active substance. Researchers strive to control for placebo effects by conducting 'blind' studies where neither the patients nor the investigators are aware as to whether an active drug or an inert substance is being dispensed. But Rabkin et al. (1986) demonstrated that, probably as a consequence of the side effects experienced, around 80 per cent of patients assigned to take the active drug in antidepressant trials break the blind and realise the group to which they have been assigned. Thus, the potential for a placebo effect is considerable.

Kirsch and Sapirstein (1998) initially highlighted the significance of placebo effects in antidepressant drug trials, estimating that 50 per cent of the reported improvement in the group taking the active drug could be attributed to a placebo effect while only 25 per cent was a consequence of the drug itself – the other 25 per cent representing spontaneous improvement that would occur without any intervention, placebo or otherwise.

Further studies by Kirsch and his colleagues (Kirsch et al., 2008; Kirsch, 2011) replicated and consolidated their earlier conclusion.

With the opportunity to access a different batch of studies, including unpublished ones acquired from the American Food and Drug Administration (FDA), they estimated that 82 per cent of the therapeutic response to antidepressants was due to the placebo effect. Furthermore, the typical difference in depressive symptoms between drug and placebo groups was so small as to be of no clinical significance to the improvement of patients' lives. Indeed, only 43 per cent of studies submitted to the FDA showed a statistically significant benefit of drugs over placebo.

In conclusion, although ingesting antidepressants may be associated with a strong therapeutic response, almost all of this effect can be attributable to a placebo effect. In other words, if an expectation of a positive outcome can be nurtured, significant benefits are likely to follow, irrespective of the type of intervention. Given the side effects and potential complications of taking antidepressants, non-chemical alternatives (physical exercise and psychological therapy for example) might be deemed to be more acceptable options.

the negative consequences of taking medication

antipsychotics

Psychiatry, in collusion with their drug-company allies, has a notorious history of sluggishness in recognising the harm associated with their physical interventions. In relation to antipsychotic medication, Peter Breggin (a long-standing critic of traditional psychiatric practices) stated, in his typically acerbic way, that 'For twenty years the profession simply failed to notice that a large percentage of its patients was twitching and writhing from the drugs' (Breggin, 1991, p. 95).

Breggin's comment referred to the movement abnormalities associated with antipsychotic use, including agitation (akathisia) and muscular rigidity. Other peculiarities, rife in the asylums from as long ago as the 1960s, include a difficulty initiating movement, a mask-like facial expression and a shuffling gait – a collective of stigmatising oddities referred to as drug-induced Parkinsonism. Subsequently, there was recognition that 30 per cent of ongoing antipsychotic users were afflicted with tardive dyskinesia, an enduring disorder characterised by uncontrollable movements of tongue, lips, face, hands and limbs, and irreversible for three-quarters of sufferers (Hill, 1986; Llorca et al., 2002). Although the aggressive marketing campaign of the 1990s trumpeted the second generation of antipsychotics (the 'atypicals') as far superior with regards to these kinds of side effects, a recent systematic review indicated that the newer class of drugs were only marginally less potent in triggering tardive dyskinesia (Correll & Schenk, 2008).

People who have acquired a 'schizophrenia' diagnosis tend to die at a significantly younger age than the general population (Osby et al., 2000; Weinmann, Read & Aderhold, 2009). Antipsychotic medications, with their deleterious effect on the body's metabolism, are likely to be an important contributory factor via their propensity to raise the levels of glucose and fats circulating in the bloodstream which, in turn, elevate the risk of heart disease, stroke and diabetes (De Hert et al., 2011). The excessive weight gain associated with antipsychotics, particularly the atypicals clozapine and olanzapine, will further inflate vulnerability to serious physical health problems (Rummel-Kluge et al., 2010).

Perhaps most disturbingly of all, there is now unequivocal evidence that antipsychotics shrink the brain. Research studies using either advanced imaging techniques or postmortem brain-tissue examination have concluded that the degree of brain-cell degeneration corresponds to the amount of antipsychotics previously ingested (Cahn et al., 2002; Dorph-Petersen et al., 2005; Arnone et al., 2009; Ho et al., 2011). Predictably, biological psychiatrists have persisted in their attempts to explain away these brain abnormalities as primarily the result of some underlying, schizophrenic-disease process (for example, Andreasen et al., 2011); they struggle to accept the stark truth that their 'treatments' are responsible for much of the observed neurological decay.

Given the brain damage caused by antipsychotics, it would be unsurprising to discover that they are associated with intellectual decline. While the research in this area is more ambiguous, some studies have raised the possibility that antipsychotic use may be responsible for accelerated cognitive deterioration in older people (Schneider, Dagerman & Insel, 2005; Torniainen et al., 2012).

For a very small proportion of antipsychotic consumers the detrimental impact can be immediate and potentially catastrophic, the drugs triggering a condition known as neuroleptic malignant syndrome. Characterised by a combination of muscle rigidity, fever and reduced consciousness, reported deaths from those suffering the disorder have ranged from 20 to 38 per cent of cases, although over recent years this figure may have reduced to less than 10 per cent (Ahuja & Cole, 2009).

antidepressants

In a striking parallel to the antipsychotic story, new types of antidepressant medication (the SSRIs) were introduced in the late 1980s, accompanied by a fanfare proclaiming both superior effectiveness and minimal side effects in comparison to their predecessors (the tricyclic antidepressants). Thirty years on, neither of these assertions has held up to scrutiny.

Moret et al. (2009) described the range of adverse consequences associated with long-term ingestion of SSRIs. Nausea, headaches and sleep disturbances are commonplace. The SSRIs also routinely impair sexual arousal and sexual performance in men and women, an unwanted additional handicap for people already struggling with depression. Further, less frequent side effects include serious complications in pregnancy, muscle cramps, disorientation, seizures, bleeds in the gut and bone fractures in older people.

Despite original claims to the contrary, it has been established that antidepressants are habit forming, and withdrawal often triggers a discontinuation effect (Double, 2011). Psychological consequences include irritability, weepiness and anxiety. Often-reported physical reactions comprise vertigo, nausea, vomiting, lethargy, insomnia, vivid dreams and electric-shock sensations in the limbs.

In conclusion, it is an ethical imperative that potential consumers of psychotropic medications are provided with accurate, non-partisan information so as to be in a position to make an informed decision as to whether the potential to realise modest benefits are worth the likely negative physical and psychological consequences. With regards to antipsychotics, it is alarming that clinical psychiatry continues to view the medication option as an essential component of any treatment programme for someone suffering with distressing voices or paranoia – hence the omnipresent prescribing across mental health services. But as Professor Anthony Morrison and his colleagues assert in a recent editorial of the *British Journal of Psychiatry* – albeit in typically hesitant academic language that may in due course be construed as the peak of irony – 'It may be time to introduce patient choice and consider whether everyone who meets the criteria for a schizophrenia spectrum diagnosis requires antipsychotics in order to recover' (Morrison et al., 2012, p. 83).

references

Ahuja, N. & Cole, A. (2009). Hyperthermia syndromes in psychiatry. *Advances in Psychiatric Treatment, 15,* 181–91.

American Psychiatric Association (APA). (1980). *Diagnostic and Statistical Manual of Mental Disorders* (3rd ed.). Washington, DC: American Psychiatric Association.

American Psychiatric Association. (2014). *Depression.* Retrieved 28 January 2014 from http://www.psychiatry.org/mental-health/depression

Andreasen, N.C., Nopoulos, P., Magnotta, V., Pierson, R., Ziebell, S. & Ho, B.C. (2011). Progressive brain change in schizophrenia: A prospective longitudinal study of first-episode schizophrenia. *Biological Psychiatry, 70,* 672–9.

Arnone, G., Cavanagh, J., Gerber, D., Lawrie, S.M., Ebmeier, K.P. & McIntosh, A.M. (2009). Magnetic resonance imaging studies in bipolar disorder and schizophrenia: Meta-analysis. *British Journal of Psychiatry, 195,* 194–201.

Baldessarini, R.J., Viguera, A.C., Faedda, G.L., Garver, D.L., Suppes, T., Tondo, L. et al. (1995). Neuroleptic withdrawal in schizophrenic patients. *Archives of General Psychiatry, 52,* 189–92.

Bentall, R.P. (2009). *Doctoring the Mind: Why psychiatric treatments fail.* London: Penguin Books.

Bola, J.R., Lehtinen, K., Aaltonen, J., Rakkolainen, V., Syvalahti, E. & Lehtinen, V. (2006). Predicting medication-free treatment responders in acute psychosis: Cross-validation from the Finnish Needs-Adapted Project. *Journal of Nervous and Mental Disease, 194,* 732–9.

Bola, J.R. & Mosher, L. (2002). Predicting drug-free treatment response in acute psychosis from the Soteria project. *Schizophrenia Bulletin, 28,* 559–75.

Bourgeois, F.T., Murthy, S. & Mandl, K.D. (2010). Outcome reporting among drug trials registered in ClinicalTrials.gov. *Annals of Internal Medicine, 153*(3), 158–66.

Braden, W., Fink, E.B., Qualls, C.B., Ho, C.K. & Samuels, W.O. (1982). Lithium and chlorpromazine in psychotic inpatients. *Psychiatry Research, 7,* 69–81.

Breggin, P.R. (1991). *Toxic Psychiatry: Why therapy, empathy and love must replace the drugs, electroshock and biochemical theories of the 'new psychiatry'.* New York: St Martin's Press.

Cahn, W., Hulshoff Pol, H.E., Lems, E.B., van Haren, N.E., Schnack, H.G., van der Linden, J.A. et al. (2002). Brain volume changes in first-episode schizophrenia: A 1-year follow-up study. *Archives of General Psychiatry, 59,* 1002–10.

Carpenter, W.T., Jr., Buchanan, R.W., Kirkpatrick, B. & Breier, A.E. (1999). Diazepam treatment of early signs of exacerbation in schizophrenia. *American Journal of Psychiatry, 156,* 299–303.

Casey, J.F., Lasky, J.J., Klett, C.J. & Hollister, L.E. (1960). Treatment of schizophrenic reactions with phenothiazine derivatives: A comparative study of chlorpromazine, triflupromazine, mepazine, prochlorperazine, perphenazine and phenobarbital. *American Journal of Psychiatry, 117,* 97–105.

Chouinard, G. & Jones, B.D. (1980). Neuroleptic-induced supersensitivity psychosis: Clinical and pharmacologic characteristics. *American Journal of Psychiatry, 137,* 16–21.

Correll, C.U. & Schenk, E.M. (2008). Tardive dyskinesia and new antipsychotics. *Current Opinion in Psychiatry, 21,* 151–6.

De Hert, M., Detraux, J., van Winkel, R., Yu, W. & Correll, C.U. (2011). Metabolic and cardiovascular adverse effects associated with antipsychotic drugs. *Nature Reviews Endocrinology, 8,* 114–26. Retrieved 15 January 2014 from http://www.rcpsych.ac.uk/pdf/De Hert_Metabolic and cardiovascular adverse effects assoc with antipsychotic drugs_Nature Reviews Endocrinology 2012.pdf

Dorph-Petersen, K.A., Pierri, J.N., Perel, J.M., Sun, Z., Sampson, A.R. & Lewis, D.A. (2005). The influence of chronic exposure to antipsychotic medications on brain size before and after tissue fixation: A comparison of haloperidol and olanzapine in macaque monkeys. *Neuropsychopharmacology, 30,* 1649–61.

Double, D. (2011). Why were doctors so slow to recognize antidepressant discontinuation problems? In M. Rapley, J. Moncrieff & J. Dillon (Eds.), *De-Medicalizing Misery* (pp. 189–96). Basingstoke: Palgrave MacMillan.

Gaebel, W., Janner, M., Frommann, N., Pietzcker, A., Kopcke, W., Linden, M. et al. (2002). First vs multiple episode schizophrenia: Two-year outcome of intermittent and maintenance medication strategies. *Schizophrenia Research, 53,* 145–59.

Gaebel, W., Weinmann, S., Sartorius, N., Rutz, W. & McIntyre, J.S. (2005). Schizophrenia practice guidelines: International survey and comparison. *British Journal of Psychiatry, 187,* 248–55.

Gilbody, S., Wahlbeck, K. & Adams, C. (2002). Randomized controlled trials in schizophrenia: A critical perspective on the literature. *Acta Psychiatrica Scandinavica, 105,* 243–51.

Gilbody, S., Wilson, P. & Watt, I. (2005). Benefits and harms of direct to consumer advertising: A systematic review. *Quality and Safety in Health Care, 14*(4), 246–50.

Goldacre, B. (2012). *Bad Pharma: How drug companies mislead doctors and harm patients.* London: HarperCollins.

Harris, G. & Carey, B. (2008). Researchers fail to reveal full drug pay. *New York Times,* 8 June. Retrieved 21 January 2014 from http://www.nytimes.com/2008/06/08/us/08conflict.html?ref=josephbiederman&_r=0

Health and Social Care Information Centre. (2012a). *Anti-depressant Prescriptions Account for Largest Annual Rise in Items Dispensed in the Community.* Retrieved 22 January 2014 from http://www.hscic.gov.uk/article/2098/Anti-depressant-prescriptions-account-for-largest-annual-rise-in-items-dispensed-in-the-community

Health and Social Care Information Centre. (2012b). *National Dementia and Antipsychotic Prescribing Audit.* Retrieved 23 January from http://bit.ly/1zUuGTo

Hill, D. (1986). Tardive dyskinesia: A world-wide epidemic of irreversible brain damage. In N. Eisenberg & D. Glasgow (Eds.), *Current Issues in Clinical Psychology.* Aldershot: Gower.

Ho, B.C., Andreasen, N.C., Ziebell, S., Pierson, R. & Magnotta, V. (2011). Long-term antipsychotic treatment and brain volumes: A longitudinal study of first-episode schizophrenia. *Archives of General Psychiatry, 68,* 128–37.

Idänpään-Heikkilä, J., Alhava, E., Olkinuora, M. & Palva, I. (1975). Letter: Clozapine and agranulocytosis. *Lancet, 2,* 611.

Iizuka, T. (2004). What explains the use of direct-to-consumer advertising of prescription drugs? *Journal of Industrial Economics, 52*(3), 349–79.

Ilyas, S. & Moncrieff, J. (2012). Trends in prescriptions and costs of drugs for mental disorders in England, 1998–2010. *British Journal of Psychiatry, 200,* 393–8.

IMS Institute for Healthcare Informatics (2012). *The Use of Medicines in the United States: Review of 2011.* Retrieved 22 January 2014 from http://www.environmentalhealthnews.org/ehs/news/2013/pdf-links/IHII_Medicines_in_U.S_Report_2011-1.pdf

Johnstone, E.C., Crow, T.J., Frith, C.D. & Owens, D.G. (1988). The Northwick Park 'functional' psychosis study: Diagnosis and treatment response. *Lancet, 2,* 119–25.

Kessler, R.C., Angermeyer, M., Anthony, J.C., Graaf, R.D., Demyttenaere, K., Gasquet, I. et al. (2007). Lifetime prevalence and age-of-onset distributions of mental disorders in the World Health Organization's World Mental Health Survey Initiative. *World Psychiatry, 6*(3), 168–76.

Kessler, R.C., McGonagle, K.A., Zhao, S., Nelson, C.B., Hughes, M., Eshleman, S. et al. (1994). Lifetime and 12-month prevalence of *DSM-III-R* psychiatric disorders in the United States: Results from the National Comorbidity Survey. *Archives of General Psychiatry, 51,* 8–19.

Khin, N.A., Chen, Y.F., Yang, Y., Yang, P. & Laughren, T.P. (2012). Exploratory analyses of efficacy data from schizophrenia trials in support of new drug applications submitted to the US Food and Drug Administration. *Journal of Clinical Psychiatry, 73,* 856–64.

Kirsch, I. (2011). Antidepressants and the placebo response. In M. Rapley, J. Moncrieff & J. Dillon (Eds.), *De-Medicalizing Misery* (pp. 189–96). Basingstoke: Palgrave MacMillan.

Kirsch, I., Deacon, B.J., Huedo-Medina, T.B., Scoboria, A., Moore, T.J. & Johnson, B.T. (2008). Initial severity and antidepressant benefits: A meta-analysis of data submitted to the Food and Drug Administration. *PLoS Medicine*, *5*(2). Available from http://www.plosmedicine.org/article/info:doi/10.1371/journal.pmed.0050045

Kirsch, I. & Sapirstein, G. (1998). Listening to Prozac but hearing placebo: A meta-analysis of antidepressant medication. *Prevention and Treatment*, *1* (Article 0002a). Retrieved 15 May 2014 from http://psychrights.org/research/Digest/CriticalThinkRxCites/KirschandSapirstein1998.pdf

Koerner, B.I. (2002). First, you market the disease … then you push the pills to treat it. *The Guardian*, 30th July. Retrieved 21 January 2014 from http://www.theguardian.com/news/2002/jul/30/medicineandhealth

Kravitz, R.L., Epstein, R.M., Feldman, M.D., Franz, Z.E., Azari, R., Wilkes, M.S. et al. (2005). Influence of patients' requests for direct-to-consumer advertised antidepressants: A randomized controlled trial. *Journal of the American Medical Association*, *293*(16), 1995–2002.

Lacoursiere, R. (1976). Medical effects of abrupt withdrawal of neuroleptic therapy. *Journal of the American Medical Association, 240*, 109.

Leucht, S., Arbter, D., Engel, R.R., Kissling, W. & Davis, J.M. (2009). How effective are second-generation antipsychotic drugs? A meta-analysis of placebo-controlled trials. *Molecular Psychiatry*, *14*, 429–47.

Leucht, S., Tardy, M., Komossa, K., Heres, S., Kissling, W., Salanti, G. et al. (2012a). Antipsychotic drugs versus placebo for relapse prevention in schizophrenia: A systematic review and meta-analysis. *Lancet, 379*, 2063–71.

Leucht, S., Tardy, M., Komossa, K., Heres, S., Kissling, W. & Davis, J.M. (2012b). Maintenance treatment with antipsychotic drugs for schizophrenia. *Cochrane Database Systematic Review, 5*, CD008016.

Llorca, P.M., Chereau, I., Bayle, F.J. & Lancon, C. (2002). Tardive dyskinesia and antipsychotics: A review. *European Psychiatry, 17*, 129–38.

May, P.R.A. (1968). *Treatment of Schizophrenia*. New York City: Science House.

Meyer, T. (1997). Two accused of medical school fraud. *Los Angeles Times*, 21 September. Retrieved 12 February 2014 from http://articles.latimes.com/1997/sep/21/news/mn-34607

Moncrieff, J. (2006). Does antipsychotic withdrawal provoke psychosis? Review of the literature on rapid onset psychosis (supersensitivity psychosis) and withdrawal-related relapse. *Acta Psychiatriac Scandinavica, 114*, 3–13.

Moncrieff, J. (2013). *The Bitterest Pills: The troubling story of antipsychotic drugs*. Basingstoke: Palgrave Macmillan.

Moore, M., Yuen, H.M., Dunn, N., Mullee, M.A., Maskell, J. & Kendrick, T. (2009). Explaining the rise in antidepressant prescribing: A descriptive study using the general practice research database. *British Medical Journal, 339*, b3999.

Moret, C., Isaac, M. & Briley, M. (2009). Problems associated with long-term treatment with selective serotonin reuptake inhibitors. *Journal of Psychopharmacology*, *23*, 967–74.

Morrison, A.P., Hutton, P., Shiers, D. & Turkington, D. (2012). Antipsychotics: Is it time to introduce patient choice? *British Journal of Psychiatry*, *201*, 83–4.

Moynihan, R. (1998). *Too Much Medicine?* Sydney: ABC Books.

Moynihan, R., Heath, I. & Henry, D. (2002). Selling sickness: The pharmaceutical industry and disease mongering. *British Medical Journal*, *324*(7342), 886–91.

National Institute for Health and Care Excellence (NICE). (2002). *Schizophrenia: Core interventions in the treatment and management of schizophrenia in primary and secondary care.* London: National Institute for Health and Care Excellence.

National Institute of Mental Health Psychopharmacology Service Center Collaborative Study Group. (1964). Phenothiazine treatment in acute schizophrenia. *Archives of General Psychiatry*, *10*, 246–58.

Neville, S. (2012). GlaxoSmithKline fined $3bn after bribing doctors to increase drug sales. *The Guardian*, 3 July. Retrieved 21 January 2014 from http://www.theguardian.com/business/2012/jul/03/glaxosmithkline-fined-bribing-doctors-pharmaceuticals

Olfson, M., Blanco, C., Liu, L., Moreno, C. & Laje, G. (2006). National trends in the outpatient treatment of children and adolescents with antipsychotic drugs. *Archives of General Psychiatry*, *63*, 679–85.

Olfson, M. & Marcus, S.C. (2009). National patterns in antidepressant medication treatment. *Archives of General Psychiatry*, *66*, 848–56.

Ornstein, S., Stuart, G. & Jenkins, R. (2000). Depression diagnoses and antidepressant use in primary care practices: A study from the Practice Partner Research Network (PPRNet). *Journal of Family Practice*, *49*, 68–72.

Osborn, D.P., Levy, G., Nazareth, I., Petersen, I., Islam, A. & King, M.B. (2007). Relative risk of cardiovascular and cancer mortality in people with severe mental illness from the United Kingdom's General Practice Research Database. *Archives of General Psychiatry*, *64*, 242–9.

Osby, U., Correia, N., Brandt, L., Ekbom, A. & Sparén, P. (2000). Mortality and causes of death in schizophrenia in Stockholm county, Sweden. *Schizophrenia Research*, *45*, 21–8.

Priebe, S., Yeeles, K., Bremner, S., Lauber, C., Eldridge, S., Ashby, D. et al. (2013). Effectiveness of financial incentives to improve adherence to maintenance treatment with antipsychotics: Cluster randomised controlled trial. *British Medical Journal*, *347*, f5847.

Rabkin, J.G., Markowitz, J.S., Stewart, J., McGrath, P., Harrison, W., Quitkin, F.M. et al. (1986). How blind is blind? Assessment of patient and doctor medication guesses in a placebo-controlled trial of imipramine and phenelzine. *Psychiatry Research, 19*(1), 75–86.

Royal College of Psychiatrists (RCP). (2014a). *Antipsychotics.* Retrieved 27 January 2014 from http://www.rcpsych.ac.uk/healthadvice/ treatmentswellbeing/antipsychoticmedication.aspx

Royal College of Psychiatrists (RCP). (2014b). *Antidepressants.* Retrieved 29 January 2014 from http://www.rcpsych.ac.uk/healthadvice/ treatmentswellbeing/antidepressants.aspx

Rummel-Kluge, C., Komossa, K., Schwarz, S., Hunger, H., Schmid, F., Lobos, C.A. et al. (2010). Head-to-head comparisons of metabolic side effects of second-generation antipsychotics in the treatment of schizophrenia: A systematic review and meta-analysis. *Schizophrenia Research, 123*, 225–33.

Safer, D.J. (2002). Design and reporting modifications in industry-sponsored comparative psychopharmacology trials. *Journal of Nervous and Mental Disorders, 190*(9), 583–92.

Schneider, L.S., Dagerman, K.S. & Insel, P. (2005). Risk of death with atypical antipsychotic drug treatment for dementia: Meta-analysis of randomized placebo-controlled trials. *Journal of the American Medical Association, 294*, 1934–43.

Shorter, E. (1997). *A History of Psychiatry: From the era of the asylum to the age of Prozac.* New York: John Wiley.

Spurling, G.K., Mansfield, P.R., Montgomery, B.D., Lexchin, J., Doust, J., Othman, N. et al. (2010). Information from pharmaceutical companies and the quality, quantity and cost of physicians' prescribing: A systematic review. *PLoS Medicine, 7*(10), e1000352

Torniainen, M., Suvisaari, J., Partonen, T., Castaneda, A.E., Kuha, A., Suokas, J. et al. (2012). Cognitive impairments in schizophrenia and schizoaffective disorder: Relationship with clinical characteristics. *Journal of Nervous and Mental Disorders, 200*, 316–22.

Verdoux, H., Tournier, M. & Bégaud, B. (2010). Antipsychotic prescribing trends: A review of pharmaco-epidemiological studies. *Acta Psychiatrica Scandinavica, 121*, 4–10.

Weinmann, S., Read, J. & Aderhold, V. (2009). Influence of antipsychotics on mortality in schizophrenia: Systematic review. *Schizophrenia Research, 113*, 1–11.

Whitaker, R. (2002). *Mad in America.* Cambridge, MA: Perseus Publishing.

Wolkowitz, O.M. & Pickar, D. (1991). Benzodiazepines in the treatment of schizophrenia: A review and reappraisal. *American Journal of Psychiatry, 148*, 714–26.

part II: currying favour

So ubiquitous is medication throughout the psychiatric system, in unison with the dominant 'illness like any other' assumptions underpinning its use, that many of the illustrative examples provided earlier in this book would effectively illustrate the issues raised in the present chapter. Therefore, only one anecdote will be provided here, recalling my experience of a drug-company representative interfacing with a community mental health team in the mid-1990s.

When I arrived for work at the community mental health centre he was there again. Sitting in the waiting area among a cluster of patients, his distinctive appearance and demeanour indicated that the purpose of his attendance did not, like the others, involve a routine injection of antipsychotic medication into his buttocks at the weekly nurse-run clinic. Dressed in a three-piece pin-striped suit, white shirt and red tie, with gleaming leather brogues that could have doubled for a mirror, he rummaged through an assortment of pamphlets in the executive briefcase on his lap.

'Who's that smartly dressed bloke in the corner?' I asked, as I signed in at the reception window.

'Oh, that's Charles, one of the drug reps. He's here to see Dr Jenkins,' replied the receptionist. 'I'm surprised you've never met him; he comes here a lot. He's lovely.' She gazed in his direction, and I thought I detected a misty glimmer in her eye.

Charles was indeed a fine-looking young man. In his late 20s with hair so dark it sometimes seemed to emit a hint of cobalt-blue, and a ruddy complexion that betrayed recent extended holidays under the Mediterranean sun, he seemed to represent the stereotypical hero in a chick-lit novel.

Later that morning, towards the end of the weekly multidisciplinary meeting attended by all the mental health professionals in the team, our manager made an announcement.

'There's no need to bring your sandwiches to this Wednesday's clinical meeting. Charles, the drug rep, has kindly offered to provide a curry and warm buffet for us all.'

Murmurs of approval reverberated across the room, and a couple of female psychiatric nurses glanced at one another, each with a knowing smile.

'We won't have to endure a lengthy sales pitch, will we?' I asked. I detected sighs from some of my colleagues, in reaction to my kill-joy comment.

'No, not at all,' said the manager. 'I've impressed upon him that he's only got five minutes to talk to us at the beginning of the meeting. He can leave a few pamphlets and other bits and bats, but that's it.'

At several points during the remainder of the day, my attention fixed on various items of drug-company paraphernalia that littered our workplace: coffee mugs in our kitchen emblazoned with motifs advertising Risperdal (an antipsychotic); coasters on the coffee tables in the reception area proclaiming the benefits of Seroxat (an antidepressant); and dozens of ballpoint pens scattered across our work desks, each extolling the virtues of Zyprexa (an antipsychotic). The imposing year-planner on our office wall, where all staff members indicated the dates they intended to take annual leave, exhibited the name, *Eli Lilly & Co.*, the pharmaceutical company who had presumably gifted it to us.

The clinical meeting happened once each month and provided an educational opportunity for the professionals in the team. Sometimes a nominated clinician would facilitate a training session on a topic requested by their peers or present a recent academic paper for discussion. Always scheduled around lunchtime, the participants typically brought sandwiches to munch while they digested the educational offerings; at this particular Charles-sponsored gathering, no such improvisation was necessary.

As I strode along the corridor towards the meeting room, I recognised the alluring vapours of chicken tikka masala. When I entered, I noticed Charles standing alongside one of the psychiatrists, engaged in vibrant conversation about one of the drug-company 'education' sheets he was distributing. I noted that he addressed the psychiatrists formally as 'doctor' while, in contrast, he chatted to the nurses using first-name familiarity. Along with my colleagues, I followed my nose to the adjacent kitchen and the food. We were greeted by a vivacious young woman (Charles' assistant) who introduced us to the fare on offer: three different curry dishes, including one suitable for vegetarians; naan bread; vol-au-vents; warm sausage rolls; an assortment of cold meat sandwiches; and an impressive range of desserts that included Black-Forest gâteau and strawberry cheesecake, each with double-cream accompaniment.

We all acknowledged the deliciousness of the lunch with mutterings of appreciation to our generous hosts.

Once everyone had filled their plates, the clinical meeting started, with Charles' 'short' presentation the first item on our agenda. Projecting multicoloured diagrams onto a screen, he shared with us the virtues of his company's new antidepressant, Seroxat (or paroxetine to use its generic name), referred to as an SSRI (the acronym for a selective serotonin reuptake inhibitor). We were shown graphs demonstrating Seroxat's marked superiority to its competitors in reducing depressive symptoms, as well as the drug's effectiveness in the treatment of anxiety disorders in general, and social phobia in particular. Charles described the elegant mode of action of Seroxat, exclusively boosting the amounts of serotonin (a chemical messenger in the brain) and how this wonder drug encouraged the growth of new brain cells.

The presentation lasted 30 minutes. Charles apologised for taking up so much of our 'precious' time. He asked if anyone wished to ask a question and I raised my hand.

'Can you show us any data about the effects of stopping this drug once you've been on it for a while?'

'It's not addictive, if that's what you mean,' said Charles. 'Seroxat is a very different drug from Valium.'

'But I wondered, when you take away the mood-boosting effects of the drug, is there not a risk that the patient will become even more depressed than they were before they started taking the medication?'

'No, no, no,' said Charles, his tone slipping towards condescension, 'the drug is rectifying an underlying chemical imbalance. There is always a risk, of course, that the illness might return if the patient ceases to take the drug. That is why we recommend maintenance treatment for at least 12 months after all depressive symptoms have disappeared.'

'But have any experiments been done comparing two groups of depressed people: those who were never treated with the antidepressant and those who were but then had the drug withdrawn?'

'I'm not sure … would we learn anything more from …,' mumbled Charles, displaying rare awkwardness and apparently struggling to know how best to respond.

'I think we need to stop there and get on with the remainder of the meeting,' the team manager interjected. 'Time is moving on.'

Charles did not offer me any of his drug-company Post-its and notepads at the end of that particular meeting.

9

a basic lack of compassion

part I: coldness and spite

The perils of construing mental health problems as products of underlying biological pathology has long been recognised, as illustrated by the following quote from a British psychiatrist, John Connolly, who in 1930 criticised the doctors who:

> have sought a strong and definable boundary between sanity and insanity which has not only been imaginary and arbitrarily placed but, by being supposed to separate all who were of unsound mind from the rest of men, has unfortunately been considered a justification of certain measures against the portion condemned which, in the case of the majority, were unnecessary and afflicting. (Cited in Clare, 1980, p. 31)

The first part of this chapter will provide an overview of psychiatry's shameful history of abusive practices, delivered under the guise of treatments, and will incorporate further details about the medical 'experts' who were the lead perpetrators of these atrocities. The astonishing negligence shown by the psychiatric profession – in their stubborn and irresponsible refusal to accept responsibility for the harm they habitually inflict on their patients – will then be described, with particular reference to the damage caused by long-term use of antipsychotic medication.

Although personal testimonies abound regarding the harmful consequences of traditional psychiatric practice, formal reporting and acknowledgement of malpractice is (with the exception of a few notorious miscreants) surprisingly rare. The likely reasons as to why institutional malpractices seldom reach the public gaze will be explored.

The second half of the chapter will offer first-hand anecdotes illustrating how coldness and spite continue unabated in our twenty-first-century psychiatric system.

historical atrocities

Psychiatry's blind faith in the idea that mental health problems are principally caused by biological disturbance has provided justification for practitioners to inflict their distinctive brand of 'treatment' onto their wretched patients, interventions that have ranged from the eccentric to the gruesome. The list that follows presents striking testimony to how an assumption of biological causation renders mentally disordered patients distinctively vulnerable to abuse at the hands of the self-proclaimed medical experts of the day.

Blood-sucking and physical assault

For many hundreds of years after Hippocrates proposed his humoral theory of mental illness in the fifth century BC (see Chapter 2, pp. 15–6), the therapeutic application of ants and leeches to the skin to extract blood endured as a common medical practice. By the nineteenth century, emetics and laxatives supplemented the blood-suckers in the common mission to expel the bodily fluids believed to cause mental disorders.

Benjamin Rush – the man responsible for publishing the first psychiatric textbook in the USA and generally regarded as the father of American psychiatry – vigorously championed blood-letting as a means of restoring sanity (Garrick, 2010). Renowned for both arrogance and paternalism, he advocated for the therapeutic benefits of aggressive purging and blood-letting, interventions he collectively described as 'depletion therapy' (Greenstone, 2010).

In the second half of the nineteenth century, a range of eccentric approaches were deployed to alleviate mental disorders, including: the simultaneous branding of a sufferer's head and feet with red-hot pokers; immersing in baths of ice-cold water; 48 hours of continuous exercise on a treadmill; and thrashing the afflicted with stinging nettles.

Around the same time, the idea emerged that insanity might be the consequence of masturbation, the best-known advocate of this bizarre notion being Henry Maudsley, an eminent British psychiatrist of the day. Maudsley lectured about insanity and worked in several county lunatic asylums. In a portent for the following century, he held the unshakeable belief that physical pathology underpinned mental illness and that genetics were the key to solving the lunatic problem; he viewed the asylum inmates as the by-products of evolution and unfit for treatment, thereby fuelling the assumption that their degeneration was inevitable (Birkbeck, University of London, 2014).

Maudsley's support for the concept of masturbatory insanity spawned the introduction of chastity belts and spiked mittens to discourage solitary sexual practices. If this strategy did not succeed, more drastic action sometimes followed, including the surgical removal of the clitoris or the severing of penile nerves.

surgical removal of organs

Another medical man, possessed by that terrible combination of God-like arrogance and an unshakeable belief that mental illness was caused by underlying physical pathology, was culpable for the mutilation and slaughter of thousands of psychiatric patients resident in an American asylum. Henry Cotton, the respected medical director of the New Jersey State Hospital in Trenton between 1907 and 1930, advocated a 'bacterial model of madness' whereby insanity resulted from infections of body parts (Scull, 2005). Armed with this warped notion, during a time when antibiotics were not yet available, Cotton concluded that the only cure for madness involved the surgical removal of the infected body part, an enterprise he pursued with reckless fervour.

The unfortunate inmates at the New Jersey State Hospital were subjected to the sequential removal of their organs and bodily parts. The teeth were extracted first. If this procedure failed to achieve the sought-after improvement in mental state, the tonsils, testicles, ovaries and colon would follow. Cotton claimed that his methods achieved the extraordinarily high success rate of 85 per cent; he did, however, acknowledge that this estimate included those who had died as they were no longer suffering!

This butchery, delivered under the guise of psychiatric treatment, continued unabated for over 20 years. Despite the fact that Cotton enthusiastically publicised his pioneering approach via lecture tours and academic papers, almost all of his medical and psychiatric colleagues lent vocal support to his methods. Around 45 per cent of his patients died as a direct result of his distinctive brand of psychiatric surgery. Thousands more were left mangled and maimed. Cotton continued his Hammer-horror-type practices until his sudden death, from a heart attack, in 1933. Some of his medical associates, however, continued with the mutilations for many more years.

inducing comas

Around the time that surgical extraction of organs was declining in popularity as a treatment for mental disorder, another brutal procedure, involving rendering patients unconscious via chemical injection, was capturing the interest of the learned psychiatric experts of the time. In the early 1930s, Manfred Sakel, an Austrian-American psychiatrist and researcher, claimed that inducing a coma through the administration of the hormone insulin achieved therapeutic effects with psychosis (Sakel, 1937).

The curative effect of insulin with diabetes (an illness characterised by dangerously high levels of glucose in the blood) had recently been established, the hormone successfully restoring the glucose level to within normal range. The administration of insulin to non-diabetic individuals produced a marked downward spiral in the levels of glucose, thereby starving the brain of sustenance and evoking first unconsciousness and, if the downward trajectory continued, subsequent death.

Throughout the 1940s and 1950s, 'insulin coma therapy' morphed into a specific treatment for schizophrenia and was enthusiastically deployed across the mental hospitals of Europe and the USA. A typical protocol involved hefty injections of insulin administered six days per week over a two-month period. The dip in blood sugar often triggered an epileptic seizure. Once a coma had been achieved, this vegetative state would be maintained for up to three hours before infusions of glucose were administered to revive the patient – an unsuccessful endeavour for up to 10 per cent of cases who died in the treatment room. The recipients of the procedure often described intense feelings of fear and suffocation at the start, and ravenous hunger in the aftermath. Many patients endured the indignity of soiling themselves during the process.

It took almost 30 years for the psychiatry profession to deduce that the treatment was ineffective, a controlled study by Ackner and Oldham (1962) finding that an insulin-fuelled coma produced no antipsychotic effects over and above a period of unconsciousness induced by other means.

Given the extent of suffering endured by the numerous victims of insulin coma therapy, it is odd that some contemporary medical commentators romanticise about the procedure. For example, Doroshow (2007) refers to this coma-inducing era as 'a key moment in the development of American psychiatry' in that it 'allowed psychiatrists to feel truly efficacious, enabling them to reinvent themselves as medical doctors' (p. 213).

slicing brains
One could be forgiven for assuming that treatments for people with mental health problems would, by the middle of the twentieth century,

have evolved into a more responsible and compassionate mode, and that crude and barbaric 'therapies' were condemned to history. On the contrary: by the 1950s thousands of psychiatric patients across the Western world were subjected to brain mutilation, delivered by a doctor armed with a mallet and an ice pick (El-Hai, 2005).

The cutting of nerve fibres that connect the front and the back of the brain, an operation known as leucotomy, was first conducted by a Portuguese neurosurgeon named Egas Moniz in 1935, an intervention that subsequently earned him a Nobel Prize. Inspired by the work of Moniz, an American neurologist and psychiatrist named Walter Freeman (along with his neurosurgeon colleague, James Watts) developed the procedure into the 'precision method' requiring the drilling of holes into the scalp.

Obsessed with his mission to discover a cure for mental illness, and frustrated that the intervention necessitated the skills of a neurosurgeon along with access to an operating theatre, Freeman simplified the approach so as to bring it within the competencies of the asylum psychiatrists. The 20-minute operation, referred to as a 'transorbital lobotomy', involved accessing the frontal lobes of the brain via the eye sockets. In Freeman's own words, the procedure consisted of:

> knocking them out with a shock and while they are under the 'anesthetic' thrusting an ice pick up between the eyeball and the eyelid … into the frontal lobes of the brain … and making the lateral cut by swinging the thing from side to side.
> (Cited in El-Hai, 2005, p. 184)

In the 1950s, Freeman travelled around America in a van he named the 'lobotomobile', demonstrating his distinctive brand of therapeutic intervention to psychiatric colleagues, describing with apparent relish how the orbital bone above the eye submitted to his ice pick with 'an audible crack'. Many children fell victim to this physician-inflicted brain mutilation, some as young as four (El-Hai, 2005).

Although a few patients gained relief from these lobotomies, many were rendered incapable of looking after themselves. Others died as a consequence of the brain damage. It has been estimated that around 40,000 lobotomies were conducted in the USA and around 17,000 in the United Kingdom (Tranøy & Blomberg, 2005).

extermination of lives deemed worthless

Without doubt, the most horrific example of where viewing mental disorders as genetically inherited brain diseases can lead is the complicity of psychiatrists in the Nazi atrocities during the Second World War.

Under the guise of protecting the sane members of society, psychiatrists oversaw a euthanasia programme targeting the mentally ill, deciding which lives were worth saving and which were expendable (Meyer, 1988; Bentall, 2009). These physicians of the mind were instrumental in designing the gas chambers and, from 1939, proceeded to systematically murder as many as 100,000 German psychiatric inmates. Even after Hitler officially ended the programme in 1941, psychiatrists in local state hospitals continued to independently cull a further 70,000. The slaughter was not restricted to Germany; around 30,000 psychiatric patients perished in occupied Poland.

current damaging treatments

Interventions that cause more harm than good cannot yet be filed away as historical aberrations in psychiatry's burgeoning skeletal cupboard. Two widespread contemporary practices are likely, with the passage of time, to be similarly condemned.

electroconvulsive therapy (ECT)

Under the misapprehension that epilepsy and schizophrenia were mutually exclusive disorders, Cerletti and Bini (two Italian neuropsychiatrists) introduced ECT in 1938 as a treatment for psychotic symptoms (Cerletti, 1956). Inspired by observing pigs being stunned in the slaughterhouse, they developed the notion that applying electricity to the brain at a sufficient voltage to evoke a seizure might rid the patient of distressing symptoms such as paranoid beliefs and hallucinations.

By the 1940s, electroshock machines were established in most asylums across the UK and USA. In these early days, the seizures triggered were so violent as to often cause fractures to limbs and ribs. The modern-day version is safer in this regard owing to the administration of anaesthetic and muscle relaxant prior to the procedure.

Despite formal guidance (NICE, 2010) continuing to recommend ECT as a last-resort treatment for severe depression, unrelenting mania or catatonia (a state of muscular stupor sometimes found in psychosis), the current use of ECT remains controversial. In practice, whether one is given ECT seems to depend as much on a person's age and gender as it does on the mental disorder (Read, 2004). In the United Kingdom, around two-thirds of recipients are women and, with regards to age, almost half are 65 or over; these skews are mirrored (or even more blatant) in most other countries, including the USA.

Established side effects of the treatment include short-term memory loss and short-term difficulties in learning new information. In addition, there is mounting evidence that ECT may cause persistent memory impairment and enduring brain damage (Read, 2004; Read et al., 2013). Recipients of ECT commonly describe an array of negative emotions including terror, humiliation and a sense of having been abused (Johnstone, 2003), a subjective response manifestly unhelpful for people with mental health problems who have often endured traumatic experiences in their lives.

Taking evidence on efficacy and side effects into account, a recent scholarly review of the literature concluded that 'the cost-benefit analysis for ECT is so poor that its use cannot be scientifically justified' (Read & Bentall, 2010, p. 333). Although the use of ECT has waned steadily over the last 30 years, many thousands of patients worldwide continue to be electrocuted under the guise of a therapeutic intervention (Breggin, 2008; Singhal, 2011). There is wide variation between psychiatric practitioners in their propensity to recommend ECT; despite the tenacity of some to habitually deploy the intervention, it seems only a matter of time before it joins the list of punitive and damaging interventions eventually discarded by psychiatry.

aggressive medication regimes for children

The indiscriminate prescribing of antipsychotics was discussed in Chapter 8. Arguably, the most disturbing example of excessive drug use in contemporary psychiatric practice is in relation to children and teenagers.

A pioneer of this particular brand of psychiatric atrocity is the American psychiatrist Joseph Biederman, who has consistently argued that over 10 per cent of children presenting to his clinic with behavioural problems are exhibiting 'a syndrome of severe, disabling psychopathology and mood dysregulation' (Biederman et al., 1996, p. 1007), subsequently referred to as paediatric bipolar disorder. According to Biederman and his associates, this alleged mental illness in children requires 'an aggressive medication regime, including anticonvulsants, lithium or a combination' (Bostic et al., 1997, p. 1487).

The tragic death of 4-year-old Rebecca Jones in Massachusetts, USA, demonstrated the potentially dire consequences of medicalising minors in this way (Able, 2007). At the age of two, a psychiatrist diagnosed Rebecca as suffering with a combination of attention deficit hyperactivity disorder (ADHD) and bipolar disorder. Subsequently she was prescribed a cocktail of potent psychotropic medication. Her parents were charged with murder after the little girl was found dead on their bedroom floor; the coroner concluded that the cause of death was intoxication due to the combined effects of the prescribed drugs and over-the-counter cold remedies.

Prior to Rebecca's death, concerns raised by social services about the severity of her drug regime were defused by reassurances from the doctors that her prescribed medication was appropriate (Cramer, 2007). At the inquest, the lawyer representing the doctor concerned stated that the diagnosis, prescribing and care provided were '100 per cent appropriate under the circumstances' and that the doctor 'did nothing wrong medically' (Kowalczyk, 2007).

denial of inflicting harm

The translation of the Hippocratic oath (a cornerstone of medical practice) includes the expressed intent to 'abstain from whatever is deleterious and mischievous' and to 'give no deadly medicine to anyone' (Gill, 2014). For a profession desperate to be recognised as a bona fide medical discipline, it is incongruous that psychiatry opts to flagrantly ignore this maxim.

As well as habitually demonstrating a gung-ho disregard for the victims of their unrelenting efforts to obliterate an assumed underlying biological pathology, the psychiatric profession continues to deny the harm associated with its current practices. A prominent example of this irresponsibility relates to the physical health costs of long-term antipsychotics.

For over 50 years, tardive dyskinesia (TD) – an enduring disorder characterised by uncontrollable movements of tongue, lips, face, hands and limbs – has been recognised to be a consequence of ingesting antipsychotic medication. In 1968, George Crane published an academic paper describing how up to 25 per cent of patients in psychiatric hospitals were afflicted with TD (Crane, 1968). His disturbing findings evoked personal attacks from fellow psychiatrists who accused him of poor scientific practice and lack of objectivity (Kline, 1968; Moncrieff, 2013, p. 78). In addition, the response included the familiar claims that pre-existing brain damage, inherent to the schizophrenic disease, was responsible for the movement disorders. Over subsequent decades, psychiatrists continued to deny the existence of antipsychotic-related TD (for example, Crow et al., 1983) or to blame it on the underlying illness: 'After age 40 the prevalence of spontaneous dyskinesia is sufficiently high to conclude that many patients with diagnoses of tardive dyskinesia have abnormal movements attributable to causes other than neuroleptics' (Knot & Wyatt, 1991, p. 661).

When not issuing absolute denials of the existence of antipsychotic-induced TD, several commentators have striven to minimise the impact of the iatrogenic disorder. Thus, while formally acknowledging that antipsychotics cause TD, an American 'task force' of academics and clinicians concluded that, 'In our opinion, the antipsychotic drugs are uniquely necessary to the effective treatments of schizophrenic illnesses. The limited information available on tardive dyskinesia ... must be utilized with this fact in mind' (Freedman, 1973, p. 463). And despite the evidence that 30 per cent of ongoing antipsychotic users will be afflicted with TD, three-quarters of whom will never recover (see Chapter 8), the website of the National Alliance on Mental Illness (a huge American advocacy group) continues to reassure its subscribers that although 'TD can be quite embarrassing ... the percentage of patients who develop severe or irreversible TD is quite low' (NAMI, 2014).

The self-serving apathy and irresponsibility of mainstream psychiatry in relation to TD was captured succinctly many years ago when Crane asserted that 'The neglect of a serious health problem for so many years has deeper roots than mere ignorance of the facts' (Crane, 1973, p. 128).

A similarly shameful mix of denial and carelessness surrounds the psychiatric profession's response to the accumulating evidence that antipsychotics may cause brain tissue to decay.

The link between shrunken brains and antipsychotics was initially proposed by Breggin in the 1980s (Breggin, 1983) and, since the turn of the century, evidence has accumulated in support of this assertion (see Chapter 8). True to form, biological psychiatrists have often denied, or at least minimised, the role of the antipsychotics (the mainstay in their treatment armoury) in eroding brain tissue. Some have resorted to their dubious default position by arguing that it is the schizophrenic illness that is responsible rather than the medication used to treat it, and that any correspondence between antipsychotic use and brain shrinkage is due to more severe illness being treated with more drugs (Arnone et al., 2009) or to a 'continuous pathophysiological process ... that warrants further study' (Hulshoff Pol & Kahn, 2008, p. 354). Others have implied only a supplementary role for deleterious drug effects: 'The loss of global gray matter in schizophrenia is progressive, occurs at an early stage of the illness, and is related to the disease process and antipsychotic medication' (Cahn et al., 2002, p. 1002).

There is even some evidence that a publication bias may operate against research studies suggesting a link between antipsychotics and brain degeneration; Moncrieff reports resistance from some academic referees to a paper she co-authored that found support for such a link (Moncrieff, 2013, pp. 156–7).

the protest against psychiatric practices

There is an abundance of first-person testimonies from service users, both in the literature and on websites, describing the injustices and invalidations experienced within the psychiatric system. Disturbing stories abound of how emotionally distressed people have been disbelieved, written off, viewed as second-class citizens and scorned by authoritarian staff (for example, May et al., 2013). Other ex-service users, such as Ted Chabasinski (now a patients' rights lawyer in the USA), have described their horrific experiences in more forceful terms. Chabasinski was removed from his dedicated foster parents at six years of age and placed in the care of a child psychiatrist only to be subsequently 'shocked and raped and tortured' (Chabasinski, 2013).

Vehicles have emerged for the purpose of mobilising the opinions of disaffected service users, and harnessing them as a means of eroding the dominance of traditional psychiatry. One outstanding example is the Intervoice and Hearing Voices Movement (Longden, Corstens & Dillon, 2013) that, as well as promoting a revolutionary new paradigm for understanding voice hearing, strives to reduce the social inequalities typically endured by people who have these experiences. Jacqui Dillon (the current Chair of the Hearing Voices Network in England) eloquently captures the passion underpinning her organisation: 'Fighting for the rights of people deemed mad, many of who have already suffered more than enough, is the last great civil rights movement' (Dillon, 2013, p. 156).

Another influential organisation is the 'Mad in America' mental health advocacy resource which, according to its mission statement, serves the needs of 'those interested in rethinking psychiatric care in the United States and abroad' (Mad in America, 2014).

However, the formal identification of institutional malpractice within mainstream psychiatric services is surprisingly rare. It is striking that a comprehensive provider of a brand of healthcare that routinely stigmatises, stifles, abuses and discriminates against the people it is commissioned to help has, for the most part, managed to avoid high-profile scandals of systemic malpractice. While other domains of state-funded care have been publicly vilified – for example, the 'cruel, callous and degrading abuse' of people with learning difficulties at the Winterbourne View care home in south Gloucestershire, England (Hill, 2012), and the 'callous indifference' shown to frail elderly people at the Mid Staffordshire Hospital, England, between 2005 and 2008 (Francis, 2013) – psychiatric services have, since the 'bedlam' of the Bethlem Hospital centuries ago, escaped widespread public censure and notoriety.

Apart from the revelations of corruption pertaining to individual psychiatrists (for example, the wrong-doings of Borison, Diamond and Biederman, discussed in Chapter 8, p. 151 & pp. 155–6), criticism of routine psychiatric practice tends only to emerge retrospectively. Even the surgical butcheries of Henry Maudsley, Henry Cotton and Walter Freeman (described earlier in this chapter) only attracted mass condemnation long after their gruesome excesses had been vented on their unfortunate patients.

Within contemporary services, why is there so little formal recognition about the pernicious consequences of traditional psychiatric practice? A number of factors may be pertinent here.

Firstly, in legal terms, there is an important difference between being unjustly treated and meeting the criterion to prove psychiatric malpractice (Degan, 2013). To show malpractice it is imperative to demonstrate that the psychiatrist under scrutiny failed to display the skills expected of other doctors in similar circumstances; since the biological paradigm dominates current services, no such discrepancy is likely to be highlighted. Furthermore, any suggestions of a causal link between psychiatric practices and harm to the patient are likely to be neutralised by assertions that it is the 'underlying illness' that is responsible.

Secondly, the powerlessness of patients (see Chapter 4) in comparison to 'expert' professionals will inevitably discourage them from making a complaint. The finding that most formal complaints received by services originate from relatives (Ingram & Roy, 1995) is consistent with this premise. The failure to believe victims' allegations regarding the serial child abuser, Jimmy Savile, starkly illustrates how the testimonies of vulnerable people tend be disbelieved (BBC News UK, 2012).

Thirdly, it is questionable whether the scrutinising bodies tasked with ensuring quality of mental health provision are fit for purpose. In England, since 2009, the Care Quality Commission (CQC) is the independent regulator responsible for the inspection of health and social care provision. (From 2004 to 2009 the inspection role was performed by the Commission for Healthcare Audit and Inspection, and prior to 2004 the responsible body was the Commission for Health Improvement.) Along with the commissioners and professional bodies, these regulators are charged with maintaining high standards and detecting misconduct.

The formal investigation into the Mid Staffordshire Hospital (Francis, 2013) concluded in its executive summary that these scrutinising bodies were ineffective in identifying malpractice and poor standards of care. The methodology employed by the inspection bodies when evaluating a mental health service has been criticised for its superficial nature, involving brief visits to the site in question and an overemphasis on risk issues (Holloway, 2001; Oyebode, Berisford & Parry, 2004). Given that the scrutinising bodies also have responsibility for physical health services it is inevitable that they will apply medical-model criteria to mental health, an extrapolation that is both dubious and deleterious.

Considering the current situation of a regulator with its methodology skewed in favour of an 'illness like any other' approach, in tandem with a psychiatric service that harbours a dominant medical model-paradigm maintained by vested interests, it seems inevitable that there will be a lengthy time-lag before today's ongoing scandals are widely exposed.

references

Able, D. (2007). Hull parents arrested in girl's poisoning death. *Boston Globe*, 6 February. http://www.astraeasweb.net/politics/riley.html

Ackner, B. & Oldham, A.J. (1962). Insulin treatment of schizophrenia: A three-year follow-up of a controlled study. *The Lancet, March 10, 1*(7228), 504–6.

Arnone, G., Cavanagh, J., Gerber, D., Lawrie, S.M., Ebmeier, K.P. & McIntosh, A.M. (2009). Magnetic resonance imaging studies in bipolar disorder and schizophrenia: Meta-analysis. *British Journal of Psychiatry, 195*, 194–201.

BBC News UK. (2012). *Jimmy Savile Scandal: Alleged victims' stories*. Retrieved 18 March 2014 from http://www.bbc.co.uk/news/uk-20066529

Bentall, R.P. (2009). *Doctoring the Mind: Why psychiatric treatments fail*. London: Penguin Books.

Biederman, J., Faraone, S., Mick, E., Wozniak, J., Chen, L., Ouellette, C. et al. (1996). Attention-deficit hyperactivity disorder and juvenile mania:

An overlooked comorbidity? *Journal of American Academic Child and Adolescent Psychiatry, 35,* 997–1008.

Birkbeck, University of London. (2014). *Deviance, Disorder and the Self: Henry Maudsley.* Retrieved 6 March 2014 from http://www.bbk.ac.uk/deviance/ biographies/maudsley.htm

Bostick, J.Q., Wilens, T., Spencer, T. & Biederman, J. (1997). Juvenile mood disorders and office psychopharmacology. *Pediatric Clinician North America, 44,* 1487–503.

Breggin, P. (1983). *Hazards to the Brain.* New York: Springer.

Breggin, P. (2008). *Brain-Disabling Treatments in Psychiatry.* New York: Springer.

Cahn, W., Hulshoff Pol, H.E., Lems, E.B., van Haren, N.E., Schnack, H.G., van der Linden, J.A. et al. (2002). Brain volume changes in first-episode schizophrenia: A 1-year follow-up study. *Archives of General Psychiatry, 59,* 1002–10.

Cerletti, U. (1956). Electroshock therapy. In F. Marti-Ibanez, R.R. Sackler, A.M. Sackler & M.D. Sackler. (Eds.), *The Great Physiodynamic Therapies in Psychiatry: An historical reappraisal* (pp. 91–120). New York: Hoeber-Harper.

Chabasinski, T. (2013). Justina Pelletier case shows public that psychiatric power is out of control. *Mad in America – Science, Psychiatry & Community.* Retrieved 25 February 2014 from https://www.madinamerica. com/2013/12/justina-pelletier-case-shows-public-psychiatric-power-control/

Clare, A. (1980). *Psychiatry in Dissent: Controversial issues in thought and practice* (2nd ed.). London: Tavistock Publications.

Cramer, M. (2007). DSS dropped inquiry before girl, 4, was found dead. *Boston Globe,* 8 February. Retrieved 25 February 2014 from http://www. astraeasweb.net/politics/riley.html

Crane, G.E. (1968). Dyskinesia and neuroleptics. *Archives of General Psychiatry, 19,* 700–3.

Crane, G.E. (1973). Clinical psychopharmacology in its 20th year. Late, unanticipated effects of neuroleptics may limit their use in psychiatry. *Science, 181,* 124–8.

Crow, T.J., Owens, D.G., Johnstone, E.C., Cross, A.J. & Owen, F. (1983). Does tardive dyskinesia exist? *Modern Problems of Pharmacopsychiatry, 21,* 206–19.

Degan, P.E. (2013). What is psychiatric malpractice? *National Empowerment Center – Articles.* Retrieved 22 February 2014 from http://www.power2u. org/articles/legal/malpractice.html

Dillon, J. (2013). The personal is the political? In M. Rapley, J. Moncrieff & J. Dillon (Eds.), *De-Medicalizing Misery* (pp. 141–57). Basingstoke: Palgrave Macmillan.

Doroshow, D.B. (2007). Performing a cure for schizophrenia: Insulin coma therapy on the wards. *Journal of the History of Medicine and Allied Sciences*, 62(2), 213–43.

El-Hai, J. (2005). *The Lobotomist: A maverick medical genius and his tragic quest to rid the world of mental illness.* New York: Wiley.

Francis, R. (2013). *The Report of the Mid Staffordshire NHS Foundation Trust Public Inquiry.* London: The Stationery Office.

Freedman, D.X. (1973). Neurological syndromes associated with antipsychotic drug use: A special report. *Archives of General Psychiatry*, 28, 463–7.

Garrick, M.L. (2010). Bloodletting 1854. *American Journal of Psychiatry*, 167(12), 1435–6.

Gill, N.S. (2014). *Is 'First Do No Harm' from the Hippocratic Oath? Myth vs fact.* About.com. Ancient/Classical History. Retrieved 12 March 2014 from http://ancienthistory.about.com/od/greekmedicine/f/HippocraticOath.htm

Greenstone, G. (2010). The history of bloodletting. *British Columbia Medical Journal*, 52(1), 12–14.

Hill, A. (2012). Winterbourne View care home staff jailed for abusing residents. *The Guardian*, 26 October. Retrieved 18 March 2014 from http://www.theguardian.com/society/2012/oct/26/winterbourne-view-care-staff-jailed

Holloway, F. (2001). The inspector calls: The CHI comes to town. *Psychiatric Bulletin*, 25, 457–8.

Hulshoff Pol, H.E. & Kahn, R.S. (2008). What happens after the first episode? A review of progressive brain changes in chronically ill patients with schizophrenia. *Schizophrenia Bulletin*, 34(2), 354–66.

Ingram, K. & Roy, L. (1995). Complaints against psychiatrists: A five year study. *Psychiatric Bulletin*, 19, 620–2.

Johnstone, L. (2003). A shocking treatment. *The Psychologist*, 16(5), 236–9.

Kline, N.S. (1968). On the rarity of 'irreversible' oral dyskinesias following phenothiazines. *American Journal of Psychiatry*, 124, 48–54 (Supplement).

Knot, V. & Wyatt, R.J. (1991). Not all that moves is tardive dyskinesia. *American Journal of Psychiatry*, 148, 661–6.

Kowalczyk, L. (2007). Psychiatrist to suspend practice; denies wrongdoing. *Boston Globe*, 8 February. Retrieved 22 February 2014 from http://www.astraeasweb.net/politics/riley.html#20070208b

Longden, E., Corstens, D. & Dillon, J. (2013). Recovery, discovery and revolution: The work of Intervoice and the Hearing Voices Movement. In S. Coles, S. Keenan & B. Diamond (Eds.), *Madness Contested: Power and practice* (pp. 161–80). Ross-on-Wye: PCCS Books.

Mad in America. (2014). *Mission Statement.* Retrieved 16 March 2014 from https://www.madinamerica.com/about-us/

May, R., Smith, R., Ashton, S., Fontaine, I., Rushworth, C. & Bull, P. (2013). Speaking out against the Apartheid approach to our minds. In S. Coles, S. Keenan & B. Diamond (Eds.), *Madness Contested: Power and practice* (pp. 233–46). Ross-on-Wye: PCCS Books.

Meyer, J.E. (1988). The fate of the mentally ill in Germany during the Third Reich. *Psychological Medicine, 18,* 575–81.

Moncrieff, J. (2013). *The Bitterest Pills: The troubling story of antipsychotic drugs.* Basingstoke: Palgrave Macmillan.

National Alliance on Mental Illness (NAMI). (2014). *Tardive Dyskinesia.* Retrieved 26 February from http://bit.ly/1tJtC10

National Institute for Health and Care Excellence (NICE). (2010). *Guidance on the Use of Electroconvulsive Therapy: An update.* Technology Appraisal 59.

Oyebode, F., Berisford, G. & Parry, L. (2004). Commission for Health Improvement and mental health services. *Psychiatric Bulletin, 28,* 238–40.

Read, J. (2004). Electroconvulsive therapy. In J. Read, L.R. Mosher & R.P. Bentall (Eds.), *Models of Madness: Psychological, social and biological approaches to schizophrenia* (pp. 85–99). London: Routledge.

Read, J. & Bentall, R.P. (2010). The effectiveness of electroconvulsive therapy: A literature review. *Epidemiology and Psychiatric Sciences, 19*(4), 333–47.

Read, J., Bentall, R.P., Johnstone, L., Fosse, R. & Bracken, P. (2013). Electroconvulsive therapy. In J. Read & J. Dillon (Eds.), *Models of Madness: Psychological, social and biological approaches to psychosis* (2nd ed.; pp. 90–104). London: Routledge.

Sakel, M. (1937). The origin and nature of the hypoglycemic therapy of the psychoses. *Bulletin of the New York Academy of Medicine, 13*(3), 97–109.

Scull, A. (2005). *Madhouse: A tragic tale of megalomania and modern medicine.* London: Yale University Press.

Singhal, A. (2011). ECT and its place in the management of depression. *Progress in Neurology and Psychiatry, 15,* 19–26.

Tranøy, J. & Blomberg, W. (2005). Lobotomy in Norwegian psychiatry. *History of Psychiatry, 16*(1). Retrieved 11 March 2014 from http://www.geocities.ws/jordotradini_/fil24.pdf

part II: if I don't think you're mad, you must be bad

'let her go; she doesn't have a genuine mental illness'

A young woman leapt from the motorway bridge. The eyewitness said that she landed feet first, her legs crumpling, an instant before she was struck a glancing blow by a white transit van, the impact catapulting her onto the grass verge.

Fortunately, she survived, albeit with multiple fractures of her legs and ribs. The life story of the casualty, 26-year-old Jenny, was depressingly familiar. Repeatedly raped by her stepfather between the ages of 5 and 10, she was taken into the care of the local authority where she remained throughout her early teenage years. While in care she developed a drug habit, routinely using heroin, barbiturates and tranquillisers (whichever she could acquire) to dampen her emotional pain. At the age of 17 she entered into a relationship with a man in his 30s, a drug-dealing pimp, who forced Jenny into prostitution and frequently battered her if she expressed any reluctance to perform the role. At the age of 21 she escaped from her life as a street walker, fell in love for the first time with a man of similar age, and became a mother to a little girl. During this relatively stable period in her life, she markedly reduced her drug use and worked part time as a secretary. Sadly, at 24 she discovered that her partner was involved in a sexual liaison with a neighbour. The relationship ended, Jenny reverted to heavy drug misuse and, as a result of her perpetual intoxication, she lost custody of her daughter.

Jenny's first encounter with psychiatric services had occurred six months prior to the bridge-jumping incident. In addition to an escalating sequence of self-mutilating acts, she had taken a hefty drug overdose that required several days on a life-support machine in the intensive care unit to revive her. Prior to this suicide attempt, she had left a note for her daughter, expressing her love while apologising for being a 'fucked-up mum'.

A combination of profoundly low mood, hearing derogatory voices, expressions of hopelessness and habitual self-mutilation had resulted in her admission to the psychiatric inpatient unit. After some instances of self-cutting on the ward, within three weeks Jenny's mental state had stabilised. She had, for the first time in her life, accepted help – the offer of referral to the specialist drug-misuse team and my invitation to engage in psychological therapy to explore ways of countering her fluctuating moods and self-loathing. There appeared to be grounds for optimism until, unexpectedly, her mother arrived at the unit to visit her.

It later emerged that Jenny had always been blamed for the break-up of the relationship between her mother and the abusive stepfather. During the visit to the ward, her mother had repeated these accusations; an argument had followed during which many disparaging comments passed between them. After her mother had left, Jenny expressed feelings that oscillated between rage and despair, and the nursing staff on the ward found it difficult to manage her challenging behaviour. Later in the afternoon, Jenny told staff she wanted to leave the ward and kill herself – 'Do it properly this time' – because there was nothing worth living for. What happened next, in the prelude to her leaping from the motorway bridge, became the focus of an internal investigation (referred to as a 'team management review') to explore if there were any lessons we could learn from this 'serious untoward incident'.

The review was chaired by a senior manager. Around 12 mental health professionals attended, all of whom had had some involvement with Jenny during her time on the ward, including: Dr Pritchard, the consultant psychiatrist; the matron and ward manager (both senior nurses); Jenny's key worker, Anne, the nurse responsible for developing and implementing an appropriate care plan; other qualified and assistant nursing staff who were working on the ward at the time of the incident; and me, the psychologist. In addition, a police officer was in attendance, the one first on scene after Jenny plunged from the bridge.

Anne, a compassionate lady in her 50s, still visibly upset by the incident, provided the review meeting with the background details – summarising the circumstances surrounding Jenny's admission to the ward, the positive changes Jenny seemed to be seeking, and the argument following the unplanned visit of her mother.

'Jenny was extremely upset after her mother left,' said Anne, 'and I'd never witnessed her so distraught. She was asking to leave the ward and, given her mental state and previous history of suicide attempts, I was concerned for her welfare. So I bleeped Dr Pritchard and asked him to review her.'

'This patient is well known to me,' said Dr Pritchard, 'and her diagnosis is clearly that of an emotionally unstable personality disorder. She is a very troubled young woman.'

'So did you see her before she left the ward?' asked the senior manager.

'Yes, I dropped what I was doing and came straight over – this type of patient tends to be very effective at raising the nursing staff's anxieties – but when I assessed her she was no different to how I'd seen her on many other occasions.'

'And how was that?' asked the senior manager.

'Typical personality disorder presentation, with lots of threats to end her life. I think she wanted me to prescribe more medication, but I'd already impressed on her a few days earlier that, as she did not have a formal mental illness, there was no justification for her to continue on antipsychotics. And I wasn't going to give her Valium again given her history of drug dependence.'

'Yes, Jenny was always asking us for medication,' said the ward sister, 'and making suicide threats; her acting-out behaviour often made it difficult for us to give time to the other patients on the ward who were very unwell.'

Some of the other nursing staff offered further anecdotes of Jenny's frequent, unrealised threats to harm herself while on the ward, and other forms of 'attention seeking', to lend support to the views expressed by their consultant and ward sister.

Prior to this team review meeting I had made a pledge to myself to try to remember the stressful roles the inpatient doctors and nurses routinely perform, and to be sensitive to the dilemmas they encounter. But at this point I felt the need to interject.

'I know we now have the benefit of hindsight, but in light of Anne's concerns (and clearly Anne is the staff member who knows Jenny best); her previous history of near-fatal suicide attempt; the knowledge that people who acquire this type of diagnosis often do kill themselves; and the awareness that the visit of her mother had probably stirred up a lot of feelings surrounding her childhood trauma – would it not have been appropriate to assume that risk was high in this instance and shown this woman some compassion?'

Heavy silence ensued for a few seconds.

'Patients with this diagnosis often kill themselves by accident,' said Dr Pritchard. 'It would not surprise me if this latest incident was not just another example of her trying to elicit caring responses from others, but on this occasion it went terribly wrong. She may well have accidentally slipped off the motorway bridge.'

'No, the evidence does not support that view in this case,' said the policeman. 'The eyewitness described how the victim climbed over the railings, glanced down at the north-bound carriageway for approximately five seconds, before proceeding to propel herself into the path of oncoming traffic. Also, the CCTV footage we have is consistent with this account.'

'Let's get back to the details of her departure from the ward,' said the senior manager, perhaps sensing the growing discomfort in the room.

'I tried to persuade her to stay on the ward, at least for another night,' said Anne, 'but she wouldn't listen. She was hysterical, saying she was going to kill herself and do it properly this time and repeatedly banging on the ward door to be let out. I was extremely concerned about her safety.'

'So what did you do?' asked the senior manager.

'I went to find Dr Pritchard again, and caught up with him in the main corridor. I told him of my concerns and said I think we should retain her for a while, at least overnight until she'd calmed down.'

'What did Dr Pritchard say?' asked the senior manager.

Anne hesitated. 'He said, "Just let her go", said something about her not having a formal mental illness, and refused to discuss it any further.'

'I have no recollection of that conversation,' said Dr Pritchard.

In the aftermath of this meeting, professional relationships were strained. One of the senior nurses on the ward accused me of unfairly criticising and undermining her nursing staff. Other nurses complained that I had been disrespectful to 'their' consultant. Various reviews were undertaken exploring how the inpatient unit responds to people with emotionally unstable personality disorder. The psychiatrists engaged in a series of meetings with senior managers (meetings myself and other professional groups were excluded from), allegedly to discuss the problems caused by people with personality disorders who presented to the inpatient unit. No member of staff faced disciplinary action.

mad or bad?

At the beginning of this chapter reference was made to the perils associated with biological psychiatry's arbitrary boundary between the sane and the insane. One stark illustration of the negative consequences of this assumed division is the apartheid approach to distressed people in the form of differentiating those with 'proper' mental illness from those assumed to be afflicted with personality disorders (difficulties characterised by enduring patterns of maladaptive behaviour, thoughts and emotional experiences).

In late 2012, while making a coffee in the kitchen of a community mental health centre, I engaged in a conversation with a consultant psychiatrist that served to underscore the contrasting assumptions psychiatry holds about those deemed to be mentally ill and those who are not. The previous day, the two of us had disagreed in a clinical meeting about the appropriate service responses to a male patient (I will call him Tom Jackson) who had been under the care of psychiatry for over 20 years. During this time, Tom had habitually self-mutilated, made occasional threats to harm others and behaved in ways that caused disruption to the community (for example, laying his body across railway lines or threatening to throw himself off bridges). Based on the construction of a shared understanding of the development and maintenance of Tom's problems (often referred to in the psychological world as a 'formulation'), I was in the process of working with Tom and all the agencies involved (psychiatric inpatient unit, crisis team, police, community mental health team) to achieve a consistent and compassionate response to Tom so as to offer him an opportunity to escape from his self-defeating patterns of behaviour.

My kitchen interaction with the psychiatrist went something like this:

Psychiatrist: I'm not sure what you are trying to achieve with Mr Jackson.

Me: What do you mean by that?

Psychiatrist: Well, I fail to see how pandering to his every need will help him to take responsibility for his bad behaviour.

Me: Have you actually read the formulation and management plan?

Psychiatrist: Yes, I did look at it some time ago.

Me: Then you'll be aware that the overarching aim of the plan is to offer Tom an opportunity to move forward while agreeing limits on his unacceptable behaviour – a combination of carrot and stick – all delivered within a compassionate framework of supporting him to achieve the positive goals he has identified.

Psychiatrist: But what's this about him being able to gain admission to the inpatient unit any time of his choosing? Why should he get preferential access over and above my other patients who, unlike this man, suffer with severe and enduring mental illness?

Me: Not sure what you mean by 'severe and enduring mental illness', but we've had that debate before. As for his admissions to hospital, Tom has spent many extended periods of time in the inpatient unit over the last 20 years. What we recently agreed to do was to try and give Tom a sense of feeling more in control – given that he often feels completely out of control – by giving him the power to opt for a 48-hour crisis admission when he feels vulnerable so long as he hasn't self-harmed or committed a criminal offence. You and your junior doctors agreed to this plan. Yet, last week, when he presented to accident and emergency seeking such an admission the doctor turned him away!

Psychiatrist: Because he does not have a mental illness. Inpatient beds are in great demand, so we have to prioritise.

Me: How can you justify discriminating against one section of our service users?

Psychiatrist: Because those with genuine mental illness can't help themselves and need our help.

Me: And those highly distressed people who don't fall within your arbitrary mental illness categories?

Psychiatrist: They can opt to change, choose to behave differently. They should also be prosecuted if they commit criminal offences.

Me: I agree with you about prosecution. It's written into Tom's programme that he should be arrested and treated like anyone else if he breaks the law. That's the 'stick' part of the plan. But then again, I believe no one should be immune from prosecution, irrespective of the type of mental health problem; we should pay everyone the respect of treating them equally in the eyes of the law.

Psychiatrist: So you would prosecute a chronic schizophrenic for their disturbed behaviour?

Me: Yes. They shouldn't be immune from the law just because of a dubious mental illness label. That wouldn't do anyone any favours. I trust the legal process to take into account mitigating circumstances when determining how to proceed and the severity of the sentence.

Psychiatrist: I find it astonishing that you believe that psychiatric services should treat the Mr Jacksons of this world in the same way as genuinely ill people. I suppose you think he's as deserving of social security benefits as well?

Me: Yes, as deserving as anyone else. After saying that I believe we should strive to discourage any of our patients from becoming dependent on long-term benefits; we should have higher expectations.

Psychiatrist: I think you're really harsh. Many of our patients with enduring mental illness need our life-long care and support.

Me: And people with so-called personality disorders?

Psychiatrist: There's not a lot we can do for them. It's up to them to decide to get their lives back on track.

how can we improve the mental health of the population?

Having considered the catalogue of shameful practices delivered under the guise of psychiatric treatment, the corrupt and irresponsible collaborations between some prominent psychiatrists and the pharmaceutical industry, and the range of fundamental disadvantages associated with the dominant assumption that mental health problems are primarily caused by biological aberrations, one would be forgiven for feeling pessimistic about the future prospects for those afflicted. Furthermore, the 'illness like any other' paradigm continues to dominate the development and delivery of psychiatric interventions in the Western world and has permeated into the minds of the general public, so much so that those commentators who challenge the validity of the paradigm are often met with vitriolic attacks questioning their sanity, integrity or levels of compassion.

So is the prospect of achieving appropriate and enabling services for people with mental health problems no more than a pipe dream? Recent bullish ranting from the president of the American Psychiatric Association does not augur well. Jeffrey Lieberman dismissed those commentators who are critical of traditional psychiatry as 'misguided and misleading ideologues and self-promoters who are spreading scientific anarchy' (Lieberman, 2013). This esteemed leader of the world's most powerful psychiatric organisation goes on to accuse the anti-psychiatry movement of fuelling prejudice against people with disorders of the brain and mind, and (with unintended irony) suggests their accusations are comparable to homophobia – an astonishing comment given that, as recently as 1974, his profession considered homosexuality to be a mental illness. He repeats the familiar illusion that 'the scientific foundation of psychiatric medicine has grown by leaps and bounds in the last fifty years' and that his specialism is experiencing 'unprecedented scientific progress'. Clearly, vested interests inherent to biological psychiatry are not about to willingly capitulate their privileged positions.

Neither do the fates of historical innovators provide optimism that radical and sustainable changes to psychiatric practice can be realised in the future. For example, in the 1970s, an American psychiatrist named Lauren Mosher developed a radical approach to the treatment and management of acutely distressed people diagnosed with schizophrenia (Mosher, 1999). The approach, known as the Soteria project, involved minimal use of antipsychotic medication and the utilisation of small crisis-support houses staffed by non-professionals. Despite publishing around 37 papers reporting that their alternative approach was at least as effective (and much cheaper) than the traditional psychiatric approach of inpatient ward and routine drugging, their findings were largely ignored by mainstream psychiatry and the project eventually lost funding in 1983 and had to be closed down. Mosher acknowledged that his innovatory approach to acute psychosis had committed psychiatric heresy; it had 'demedicalized, dehospitalized, deprofessionalized and deneurolepticized [sic]' (Mosher, 1999, p. 148) the way mentally ill people were treated. Similar marginalisation befell Thomas Szasz, a psychiatric professor and outspoken critique of conventional practice, who was banned from teaching psychiatric trainees because of opposition from his colleagues (see Johnstone, 2000, pp. 201–19).

But maybe, as I write this chapter in the year 2014, there are a number of factors that, collectively, may achieve the urgently required shift in the way we respond to people with mental health problems.

reasons for optimism?

The unprecedented heterogeneity of individuals and groups presently condemning traditional psychiatric practice is such that it is more difficult for the old guard to dismiss them as cranks or ideological extremists. The protests regarding the damaging and relatively ineffective interventions offered by biological psychiatry emanate from an array of sources, including: the personal stories of a multitude of service users; civil rights activists, acting both individually and as a collective (for example, Mind Freedom International); organisations such as the Hearing Voices Network, whose membership comprises mental health professionals, service users, and other interested stakeholders, promoting alternative ways of making sense of mental health problems; journalists; dissident psychiatrists; and critical authors from a range of professional disciplines including clinical psychology, social work and psychiatric nursing. As such, it is increasingly difficult to ignore this collective scream of disapproval.

Importantly, there is growing recognition from within the psychiatric profession that all is not well. Indeed, perhaps for the first time since the advent of chlorpromazine in the 1950s, there have been high-profile acknowledgements that the discipline is in urgent need of a radical change of direction. For example, a recent press release from Mental Health Europe (a respected collaboration of professionals and service users) opened with the statement: 'Western psychiatry is in crisis' (Mental Health Europe, 2013). Although the publication of the latest edition of the psychiatric bible, *DSM-5*, triggered their statement – they expressed alarm at the way normal human reactions like grief and shyness had been medicalised – their criticisms of traditional psychiatry probed much more deeply into the core business of the profession. Thus, concern was expressed about the 'relative downgrading of psychological and social interventions' and the way that 'reductionist science' can 'impede understanding of the human condition and encroach on basic human rights' (Mental Health Europe, 2013).

A troupe of psychiatrists voiced further apprehensions about the current state of their profession in a special article in the *British Journal of Psychiatry* (Bracken et al., 2012). 'Psychiatry is not neurology; it is not a medicine of the brain,' they announce. And 'the evidence base is telling us that we need a radical shift in our understanding of what is at the heart (and perhaps soul) of mental health practice' (p. 432). The authors proceed to self-flagellate about psychiatry's over-endorsement of medication, 'their blindness towards the serious adverse effects of some psychiatric drugs' and 'their shameful collusion with the pharmaceutical industry's marketing campaign that sold the illusion of major innovations in antipsychotic drugs' (p. 432).

In addition to these increasing expressions of dissatisfaction from the psychiatric community, there are three further factors contributing to the creation of a fertile milieu for radical change.

Firstly, there are embryonic signs that biological psychiatry's dominance of the mental health research agenda may, in the future, be weakened. For several decades, funding for research initiatives in psychiatry has been skewed in favour of genetic, biological and pharmacological studies. However, the National Institute for Mental Health (NIMH), the largest psychiatric research institute in the world, in the aftermath of *DSM-5*, announced that they will move away from funding research based exclusively on diagnostic categories (Winerman, 2013).

Secondly, the growing number of legal actions against the pharmaceutical companies (see Chapter 8, pp. 150–1) suggests that the industry is no longer immune to formal censure, and risks heavy financial penalties should it continue with corrupt and misleading drug-marketing practices.

Thirdly, and most crucially, the political systems in Western societies face ever-increasing pressures to reduce the amount of public money dedicated to the provision of health services. By far the greatest proportion of a government's health budget is dedicated to funding the salaries of professional staff. Given the urgent need for a paradigm shift away from a medically dominated approach to mental health, together with the fact that the remuneration for consultant psychiatrists dwarfs that of all the other staff groups, it is feasible to propose that a much improved mental health service could be provided for significantly less money. Such a prospect would inevitably appeal to taxpayers and health ministers alike, and could inspire the political commitment that is essential if radical change is to be realised.

how can we improve people's mental health?

So if a number of levers for change are coming together to provide a fertile context for the development of an alternative, more appropriate kind of mental health service, how can we seize the moment and achieve the required transformation in the way we respond to people suffering emotional distress?

To eliminate the fundamental flaws in current psychiatric provision – which, as already described, include unethical levels of coercion, the promotion of stigma and passivity, the damaging overuse of medication, the crushing of people's aspirations, a suffocating obsession with risk, and an inherent lack of compassion – will necessitate significant changes across a range of domains, including the social and political. The achievement of the desired transformation will, therefore, require revisions at different levels of our society, in addition to a radical shake-up of psychiatric services per se.

For ease of description, the following account will firstly address the benefits that could be realised by expanding and promoting existing elements of good practice within the current psychiatric system. However, these developments in isolation are unlikely to be sufficient to attain the paradigm shift required to avert the development of mental health problems, and to respond to them appropriately once they have emerged. Therefore the second part of this section will propose some more radical, whole-system changes that are essential if we as a society are to effectively respond to human suffering.

change through supporting existing positive practice

One of the more encouraging aspects of contemporary mental health services has been the promotion of a 'recovery approach' (Repper & Perkins, 2012), where the emphasis is on adherence to a set of values and principles believed to be instrumental in enabling people suffering with mental disorders to live meaningful lives (see Chapter 5, pp. 85–6 and Chapter 7, pp. 125–6). Active engagement with life, participation in worthwhile activities, the maintenance of hope and the achievement of personal goals are all highlighted to be as important, if not more so, than the elimination of psychiatric symptoms.

Continuing investment, both financially and strategically, to ensure that a recovery mentality permeates into every part of mental health services, would represent an important evolution in provision. Such a development does, however, represent a formidable organisational challenge to psychiatric services that cling to a medical, 'illness like any other' approach and there is a real risk that a recovery orientation remains nothing more than an aspiration. Helpfully, formal guidance exists that both highlights the main organisational challenges (for example, to deliver training programmes led by the service users and to increase opportunities for building a life 'beyond illness') and proposes ways by which they can be successfully negotiated (Sainsbury Centre for Mental Health, 2009).

One promising initiative for challenging the prevailing culture within psychiatric services involves the development of Recovery Education Units (or Recovery Academies), a service-user-led training initiative to provide a rolling programme of recovery-informed courses, available to all (professional staff, service users and interested lay people). Educational establishments of this kind have already emerged across the Western world, including the United Kingdom, where service users (or 'experts by experience') develop and deliver training courses alongside professional staff. Furthermore, service users are offered the opportunity to train as paid peer professionals and work alongside traditional mental health professionals as direct care staff; although this initiative is in its infancy, transforming the workforce so as to include a greater proportion of people with lived experience of mental health problems would help facilitate the required culture change within core services. To meaningfully develop and sustain Recovery Academies will require recurring investment to fund the skilled leadership and supervisory networks essential to enable this initiative to flourish and make a difference.

Another essential goal of a recovery-orientated service is to achieve collaborations with a range of community resources. Enabling service users to retain, or develop, valued roles is often a major factor in facilitating a return to positive mental health. Mental health workers dedicated to facilitating links between mainstream psychiatric services and community facilities (offering educational, vocational and leisure opportunities) already exist, albeit in a peripheral form, and regrettably these types of provision tend to be the first to be cut in order to meet an organisation's financial targets. A refocusing of investment is required in favour of service components that help service users find employment (paid or voluntary), college courses and pastimes within their local communities.

Meaningful service user involvement in every aspect of provision – service development, staff selection, staff training, governance committees and service delivery – is a mantra often espoused by specialist mental health organisations. Regrettably, in practice, the involvement of people with lived experience of mental health problems in an organisation's core activities can seem tokenistic; a solitary service user among a 20-strong group of senior managers and high-status professionals, for example, is unlikely to achieve any meaningful impact on service delivery. Barriers to achieving consequential service user involvement include resistance from professionals and the financial cost to service users, who may often receive inadequate levels of payment for their time and travel expenses (Tait & Lester, 2005). Existing examples of positive practice could be usefully replicated, although cultural resistance to change, particularly in the form of reticence to the concept of genuine service-user–professional partnerships, is likely to present a formidable obstacle (Crawford et al., 2003; Tait & Lester, 2005).

Perhaps the most successful area of service user activity to date has been in the realm of direct provision of services such as drop-in centres, support groups, phone lines and advocacy programmes. These initiatives typically adhere to a number of principles, including: being run and managed by people with lived experience of mental health problems; a model of peer support rather than professional expertise; and a commitment to minimise hierarchy and to value the contributions of every participant (Dillon et al., 2013). Several studies have found that initiatives of this type produce positive outcomes, including enhanced wellbeing, greater satisfaction with services, reduced distress and hospitalisation, expanded social networks, enhanced self-esteem; and general improvement in the quality of life (for a review, see Dillon et al., 2013, pp. 308–10). The essence of the value of peer support is captured by the assertion that the first experience of meeting someone with similar problems in a group or day centre can be a significant turning point in a person's life, 'emphasizing the value of acceptance and belonging against a background of stigma and discrimination' (Dillon et al., 2013, p. 310). In times of global constraints on healthcare budgets, it would be prudent to invest further in user-run services.

Government investment in service-user-led organisations that promote an alternative way of making sense of mental health problems would also be helpful as a means of improving current provision. An outstanding example of an alternative approach is the Hearing Voices Network (HVN) (Longden, Corstens & Dillon, 2013). The HVN provides the opportunity for people experiencing voice hearing or visions to talk freely in a supportive environment immune from the risks of censure, incarceration and forcible medication. Since its inception in the 1980s, and with limited funding, the HVN has developed over 200 groups across England and many more in multiple countries across Europe, North America, Asia, Australia and Africa, in the process enabling many people with distressing mental experiences to break their reliance on statutory services. With the benefit of more government funding, its impact could be considerably greater.

While acknowledging the central role of past life experiences (abuse, discrimination and inequality) in the development of mental health problems, it is crucial that sufferers are afforded easy access in the here and now to a wide range of interventions to reduce distress and misery. Such a menu of change techniques, including the talking therapies, medication, peer support and self-help guidance, should be routinely available together with balanced information describing the pros and cons of each approach, so that each person can make an informed decision as to whether to opt in. To achieve this comprehensive provision would again require a significant redistribution of central funding away from the dominant psychiatric mode of medicating, risk-assessing and monitoring mental state.

how can we become more effective at challenging the dominant medical paradigm?

Clinicians within the contemporary psychiatric services often claim that their individual practice, and that of their teams, is informed by a 'bio-psycho-social' approach to mental health problems, a mantra implying that assessment and treatment approaches give equivalent gravitas to the three domains (biological, psychological and social) of each patient. In actuality, this is far from the case. If a person's social milieu or psychological processes are addressed at all they will typically be seen as secondary to the underlying biological illness – additional add-ons to the fundamental brain pathology.

Boyle (2013) poses the crucial question of why the medical-model understanding of mental health problems continues to dominate psychiatric practice despite flimsy empirical support and mounting evidence of its negative impact upon service users. One reason suggested relates to the 'brain or blame' notion – the assumption (sometimes implicit, often explicit) that challenging the view that mental health problems are primarily the product of brain aberrations is tantamount to blaming the sufferers (or their families) for the affliction. This is not a recent phenomenon; as already mentioned (p. 192), Szasz was ostracised decades ago for challenging the validity of biological notions of mental illness. Given the evidence that 'illness like any other' assumptions are inherently associated with dismissive attitudes (see Chapter 3, pp. 43–4) and punitive service responses (see Chapter 9, pp. 170–6), the 'brain or blame' fallacy is a paradoxical one. It would therefore be useful if all mental health professionals challenge this myth wherever it is encountered.

A useful way of making sense of how medicalisation of mental health problems stubbornly persists within Western psychiatric services is to highlight how alternative approaches are neutralised. Boyle (2013) provides a helpful framework for understanding this process by suggesting that there are two main ways by which non-biological perspectives are nullified. The first, being ridicule and personal attacks directed towards the person offering the alternative viewpoint, a process referred to as 'invalidation'. The second, and arguably the more difficult to counter, is a process Boyle describes as 'assimilation' whereby the more radical aspects of the new idea are removed so that what remains appears different from the dominant orthodoxy only in degree of emphasis. In these circumstances, proponents of the medical-model approach to mental health problems are able to claim that the 'new' idea is not really new and that the practices of the existing service are already broadly consistent with it.

One illustrative example of assimilation I recently encountered occurred in the context of a statement from the Division of Clinical Psychology (DCP, 2013) – a UK national body representing the interests of the clinical psychology profession – asking, in the aftermath of *DSM-5*, for a paradigm shift away from the routine use of narrow diagnostic categories for making sense of mental health problems. In the specialist mental health Trust where I was working, this DCP statement was circulated to all senior clinicians for their comments; the lead psychiatrist responded that the proposal had little relevance to our place of work, as 'My psychiatry colleagues and I are social psychiatrists who are not wedded to diagnoses'. Such an assertion seemed in stark contrast to the weekly interchanges between my psychiatry colleagues at the multidisciplinary team meetings about whether a particular patient's presentation corresponded to 'schizophrenia', 'schizo-affective disorder' or 'bipolar disorder'.

The claim to be 'social psychiatrists' has also been used in the literature by those expressing dissatisfaction with the current paradigm and, although it is welcome to hear psychiatrists emphasising the importance of relationships and the interpersonal context, elements of their discourse suggest attempts to assimilate new ideas while ensuring they, the medical specialists, continue to perform their leadership roles. Thus, Bracken et al. (2012) assert that 'the problems we grapple with cry out for a more nuanced form of medical understanding and practice', and go on to propose that 'psychiatry has the potential to offer leadership' (p. 432). Similarly, Priebe, Burns and Craig (2013) state that 'embracing a social paradigm could generate real progress and, simultaneously, make the profession more attractive', and subsequently remind us that this revised brand of psychiatric practice will not involve 'in any way diluting its core medical responsibility' (p. 320). So the underlying message seems to be that, as social psychiatrists, they are able to adopt this more intuitive, interpersonally sophisticated form of practice where, despite their distinctive biological expertise no longer being central to the treatment of people with mental disorders, the medical specialists remain in charge (Johnstone, Dillon & Fernando, 2013).

How can this assimilation and neutralisation of new ideas be effectively countered? Boyle (2013) persuasively argues for the abandonment of the routine adoption of language associated with physical illness – terms such as symptoms, treatments and disorders. Within contemporary psychiatric services, this medical terminology is habitually used by a range of mental health professionals (psychiatrists, psychologists, psychiatric nurses, social workers, occupational therapists), even those committed to offering alternative perspectives to the dominant orthodoxy. Continued use of medical language can give the impression that any disagreement with biological psychiatry is only superficial and that, fundamentally, all parties are talking about the same thing:

> You study single symptoms of schizophrenia, I'll study schizophrenia as a whole; you study psychological aspects of bipolar disorder, I'll study biological aspects of bipolar disorder; you provide psychological treatments of mental disorders, I'll provide drug treatments for mental disorders.
> (Boyle, 2013, p. 14)

Instead of terms extrapolated from the physical illness domain, alternative approaches would possess greater immunity to assimilation if they were expressed in neutral language – for example, 'She is hearing voices condemning her as dirty and worthless in the context of having been sexually and physically abused as a child and as an adult.' If medical language is used, it could be helpfully qualified as representing a particular perspective rather than an actual description, for example, 'what some professionals might view as symptoms of depression'.

It would, of course, be absurd to ignore biology altogether. Human beings are, at a fundamental level, the product of a complex array of chemicals and, inevitably, each experience (emotional and perceptual) and all behaviour will be mediated through a biological process. Sadness and elation, voicehearing and unusual beliefs, withdrawal and overactivity – all will have their own, distinctive biological correlates. Without making the all-too-frequent mistake that a correlate is synonymous with a cause, the development of sophisticated models that explain the reciprocal relationships between life experience, social context, psychological processes and biology would be another way to prevent the neutralisation of alternative perspectives to the medical conceptualisations of misery and distress – for example, the link between childhood abuse and brain structure (see Chapter 2, p. 21).

how can we promote informed decision-making about medication?

The ubiquitous prescribing of antipsychotic and antidepressant medications has already been described (see Chapter 8, pp. 147–9). In addition to the considerable negative consequences of these excesses, this epidemic symbolises a 'pill for every ill' mentality and perpetuates the myth that mental health problems are primarily the products of biological disturbances. If alternative approaches to the reduction or alleviation of human distress and misery are to take hold, a radically different framework for informing decisions about medication use is required.

The pioneering work of Joanna Moncrieff, a British psychiatrist, offers a helpful way of thinking about how psychiatric drugs achieve their effects, thereby enabling the potential recipient to make an educated judgement as to whether or not to proceed (Moncrieff, 2008, 2013). Moncrieff describes the crucial distinction between 'disease-centred' and 'drug-centred' action when contemplating the effects of antipsychotic and antidepressant medications on the human brain. In the disease-centred view, the assumption is that the drug achieves its effect by specifically rectifying an underlying biochemical imbalance, restoring equilibrium to a pathological system (see Chapter 2, pp. 17–8). In contrast, the drug-centred view proposes that psychiatric medications realise their effects through the creation of abnormal brain states. Sometimes these chemically induced states of mind might be preferable in comparison to the alternatives – for example, sedation for someone who is highly agitated – but abnormal states they are, nonetheless. According to the drug-centred view, the ingestion of antipsychotics and antidepressants is rather like consuming alcohol to overcome shyness; there may be benefits from achieving a mildly intoxicated (abnormal) mindset.

Despite a paucity of empirical support for the notion that biochemical imbalances underpin mental disorders, psychiatrists and the pharmaceutical industry continue to energetically promote the myth that antipsychotics and antidepressants achieve therapeutic effects by restoring equilibrium to the brain. For example, the website of the American Psychiatric Association broadcasts the message that 'Antidepressants may be prescribed to correct imbalances in the level of chemicals in the brain' (APA, 2014). Advertisements by the drug companies have resorted to disease-centred language since the 1960s and the success of these campaigns is evident by the way that serotonin deficiency (as a cause of depression) and dopamine overactivity (as a cause of schizophrenia) have seeped into popular culture despite the hugely inconsistent and contradictory evidence for such links (Moncrieff, 2013, pp. 39–59).

As part of their desperate mission to promote psychiatry as a legitimate medical speciality, the psychiatric profession persists with their fallacious claims that their drug treatments achieve disease-centred effects, restoring harmony to the brain's biochemistry. Such a stance is associated with a number of other advantages for psychiatry, including: the justification of coercion by construing medication as a specific treatment for underlying disease rather than as a chemical cosh; the differentiation of psychiatric drugs from those commonly associated with recreational use, such as cocaine and amphetamine; and a better fit with a political climate striving for interventions that are quick, cheap and apparently evidence based.

To effectively counter this pernicious and widespread misconception – one that unhelpfully strengthens the 'illness like any other' ethos – will present a considerable challenge. One crucial area concerns the information, both verbal and written, offered to service users when medication is being considered as a treatment option (which would currently encompass all care review meetings and virtually all contacts with psychiatrists). Importantly, service users should be informed that they have a genuine choice as to whether or not to take medication, and that declining this treatment option is not synonymous with a diabetes sufferer refusing to take insulin; there are always alternatives (although occasionally these might not always be feasible in the short term, such as when the level of agitation is so high as to preclude most non-chemical interventions).

Furthermore, the tone of language (written and spoken) to describe the potential benefits of medication should reflect a drug-centred view of their mode of action. Therefore, references to 'treating underlying illness', 'balancing brain biochemistry' and 'correcting abnormal states' should be avoided. Instead, service users should be informed that the medication will likely induce an altered state of mind which (depending on the drug being considered) may be experienced as 'sedation', 'slowed thinking' or 'a numbing of painful emotions'. Such drug-mediated effects may, of course, be highly desirable, at least in the short term.

People suffering mental health problems should also be alerted to the potential negative effects of long-term use of medication. So, with regards to both antidepressants and antipsychotics, service users should routinely be acquainted with potential adverse consequences of ceasing the medication after a lengthy period of consumption (see Chapter 8, pp. 154–5 & p. 159). In addition, potential recipients should be made aware of the side effects of psychiatric medications. This educational process should not shy away from making reference to the sexual impairments associated with antidepressants and the evidence for brain atrophy, physical health risks and tardive dyskinesia in relation to antipsychotics (see Chapter 8, pp. 157–9).

change through whole-system transformation
Seeking significant change within the existing psychiatric system, so as to promote more appropriate (and less damaging) services for people with mental health problems, represents a noble endeavour. Building on elements of recovery-orientated practice, extending service user initiatives, changing the language by which we present new ideas so as to

immunise them against neutralisation, and promoting a 'drug-centred' way of making sense of psychiatric medications are all laudable projects. However, these collective initiatives, conducted under the banner of a health service and within existing political and legal parameters, may be insufficient to realise the required paradigm shift in how we respond to people at risk of, or already experiencing, high levels of distress and misery.

Radical, whole-system transformation is required to create the type of society that enables people to flourish. The foundation stone of this transformation would be a shift in emphasis from the current narrow focus on the treatment of 'mental illness' to the promotion of a broader, multifaceted state of mind that could be described as mental wellbeing. The World Health Organization (WHO, 2014) defined mental health as 'a state of wellbeing in which every individual realises his or her own potential, can cope with the normal stresses of life, can work productively and fruitfully, and is able to make a contribution to her and his community'. Similarly, the Government Office for Science (2008) described mental wellbeing as:

> a dynamic state, in which the individual is able to develop their potential, work productively and creatively, build strong and positive relationships with others, and contribute to their community. It is enhanced when an individual is able to fulfil their personal and social goals and achieve a sense of purpose in society. (Government Office for Science, 2008, p. 10)

It is clear, based on these definitions, that a significant improvement in people's general wellbeing cannot be realised solely by transformations of healthcare provision, but will require coordinated changes in a range of domains, including the social, vocational, economic and political.

It is reasonable to suggest that the desired paradigm shift essential to the promotion of positive mental health cannot be achieved while the major resource dedicated to this task (psychiatric services) resides under a 'health' banner. In the United Kingdom, this would involve shifting the prime responsibility for addressing human misery and suffering away from the National Health Service (NHS). The medical and nursing expertise within the NHS is ideal for responding to the physical illnesses of the general population (for example, cancer, heart disease, broken bones and respiratory problems) but should be a more peripheral contributor to the promotion of mental wellbeing. Extensive training in biological pathology does not equip a practitioner to play a central role in addressing the mental health needs of people within our communities.

Not only is the focus of the NHS inappropriate, and too narrow, to meaningfully lead initiatives to promote wellbeing, but also its culture is such as to present a formidable obstacle to the far-reaching changes required. There is persuasive evidence that organisations like the NHS remain stubbornly resistant to change despite repeated restructurings aimed at transformation (Davies, 2002). The inherent culture – the shared understanding of 'how things are done around here', evident in the beliefs and values of the workforce – often remain immune to outside interference. Formal and systematic attempts to modernise service provision are usually futile; in the words of one American chief executive, 'Culture eats strategy for breakfast, every day, every time' (cited in Davies, 2002, p. 142). Western health care systems are, rightfully, a vehicle for delivering medical expertise – an approach with its distinctive underlying assumptions (including the primary causative role of biological pathology in ill health) and visible manifestations (doctors' white coats, nurses' uniforms and professional titles). These cultural elements effectively maintain the status quo despite attempts at reform. As such, efforts to achieve meaningful changes within the current psychiatric system (as discussed above) may ultimately be a futile endeavour.

the promotion of wellbeing

To achieve a meaningful reduction in the level of human distress and misery would require a multifaceted, multilayered approach that extends far beyond the remit and competencies of physical health service providers like the NHS. Indeed, to propagate the notion that the mental health needs of the nation can best be met by the effective treatment of so-called mental illness, realised through much greater investment in existing psychiatric services, is both absurd and counterproductive; a 'more of the same' approach will only exacerbate the range of detrimental consequences (detailed throughout this book) inevitably associated with construing mental distress as if it were synonymous with physical illness.

So how can we promote mental wellbeing, and how should such an initiative be led? In light of the multifaceted changes necessary to achieve a society where people flourish, the body invested with responsibility for leading such an ambitious initiative would require not only the powers to influence and coordinate many disparate stakeholders, but also a remit to shape economic and social welfare policies. It is reasonable to propose that the realisation of these far-reaching revisions would require something akin to a dedicated government ministerial department, a Department for Wellbeing.

Coles (2013) highlighted the important contributions of disempowerment and marginalisation to the genesis of madness. Therefore, any meaningful project to promote greater wellbeing within our society will require leadership that is endowed with sufficient political clout to reduce economic inequalities, improve people's access to opportunities, and address the enduring societal ills such as unemployment and homelessness.

Early life experience is a crucial determinant of subsequent wellbeing. Social disadvantage in childhood, characterised by lack of nurture and an exposure to adverse intra-family events such as violence and abuse, is likely to be more detrimental than poverty per se in shaping future mental health (see Chapter 2, pp. 25–6 and Chapter 4, p. 67). It is therefore imperative that the interpersonal environments of our children attract the focus of a comprehensive and integrated public policy that promotes better parenting and home environments free of both neglect and abuse (Clements & Davies, 2013).

Regrettably, biological psychiatry's mendacious claim that mental illnesses are primarily caused by genetically acquired brain abnormalities has been embraced by Western governments to condone their failure to target social and economic disadvantage as a means of reducing the incidence of psychiatric disorders. The neglect of a primary prevention focus is also reflected in the dearth of research activity dedicated to exploring the impact of countering socially disadvantaged family environments on subsequent mental health, despite the fact that a rare study (Raine et al., 2003) reported that a two-year environmental enrichment programme at ages three to five reduced psychotic-like features in early adulthood.

A comprehensive and adequately funded primary prevention programme could significantly enhance the mental wellbeing of the population. There is evidence that the provision of intensive professional help targeting low-income, single mothers (referred to as Nurse–Family partnerships) can reduce the incidence of child abuse (MacMillan et al., 2009). Similarly, Early Start initiatives in the United Kingdom, involving collaborative support and the provision of advice, show promise (Donelan-McCall, Eckenrode & Olds, 2009). A systematic review of the literature concluded that interventions to counter child maltreatment (home visiting, parental education around child-rearing skills and multi-component family support) can be effective (Mikton & Butchart, 2009). Clearly, trying to remedy the pernicious impact of child adversity after the event is much more costly, with regards to both human suffering and public finances, than preventing it in the first place; such a radical change in emphasis would, however, require the political will to achieve a pronounced shift in the allocation of resources from the current 'medicate and risk management' model to one of primary prevention.

revision of the mental health act

Mental health legislation in England and Wales (the Mental Health Act, 1983, and subsequent revisions in 2007), along with other mental health policy across the Western world, represent legalised discrimination against people suffering mental distress (see Chapter 4, pp. 62–5). Under the current legislation, law-abiding citizens can be incarcerated against their will and forcibly medicated. In addition to reinforcing stereotypical links between mental illness and violence, the Mental Health Act is at odds with the United Nations Convention on the Rights of Persons with Disabilities (United Nations, 2006) which states that 'The existence of a disability shall in no case justify a deprivation of liberty.' Clearly, existing mental health law is concerned with the containment of people arbitrarily labelled as displaying a 'mental disorder' rather than with the promotion of positive mental health.

In reaction to this fundamental injustice, Sartorius (2002) asserted that 'the rights and duties of people with mental illness should be decided by their behaviour and capacities in the same manner as for other people rather than by the diagnostic label alone' (p. 1470). Szmukler (2010) develops this notion and proposes that the source of this discrimination is the existence of two independently constructed pieces of legislation, one based on the assessment of capacity (determining whether someone has the wherewithal to make their own decisions) and the other on the assessment of mental disorder – in the United Kingdom, the Mental Capacity Act (2005) and the Mental Health Act (2007) respectively.

One crucial consequence of this unsynchronised development is the upshot of two strikingly different sets of criteria to justify coercion. On the one hand, treatments for physical disorders can only be imposed when the person afflicted has lost capacity and it is deemed to be in the person's best interests. Whereas, in contrast, treatments for mental disorders can be imposed when psychiatric experts conclude that the person under scrutiny is both suffering from a formal mental illness and a risk to self or others. The outcome of this distinction is that the mentally disordered comprise a unique subgroup of risky people; in contrast to those who drink to excess, abuse drugs, drive recklessly, and so on, people with mental health problems are subjected to the imposition of preventative detention despite no history of criminal behaviour.

In order to end this blatant form of legalised discrimination, a revision of the mental health legislation is urgently required. Szmukler (2010) proposed a viable alternative in the form of a 'fusion law', a single comprehensive law addressing involuntary treatment based solely on 'capacity' and 'best interests', with no specific reference to mental disorder. Under this amended legislation, any law-abiding person with the capacity to make his or her own decisions would be immune to coercion. Conversely, along with rights come responsibilities, so presumably it would follow that mental disorder alone would not of itself constitute a legal defence against prosecution for a criminal act – although, of course, a jury would rightly consider the individual circumstances of each case.

final thoughts

The views expressed in this book are the product of my experiences associated with 33 years of continuous employment within psychiatric services. A lifetime of working as part of a system whose remit is to help people suffering misery and distress has led me (and many others) to the stark conclusion that Western psychiatric services are not fit for purpose. Despite the well-intentioned efforts of a multitude of professional staff, the dominant 'illness like any other' approach to mental suffering is both profoundly damaging and relatively ineffective in promoting recovery.

If we, as a society, are to reduce the emotional pain and anguish of people living within our communities, a radically different approach is required with regards to both the prevention of, and response to, human distress. Rather than stifling hope and motivation via the message that people are victims of their inherited brain biochemistry, an optimal approach would routinely convey the message that recovery is a feasible goal for everyone. Rather than inflicting stigma and prejudice through paternalism and discriminatory practices, an optimal approach would empower people with the confidence to take personal responsibility for working towards a better future. Rather than dedicating the bulk of our resources to the treatment of distressed adults with assumed internal defects, an optimal approach would promote wellbeing both by addressing the range of socio-economic issues that generate (and maintain) human misery, and by the provision of intensive family support to counter child maltreatment. And rather than the ubiquitous prescribing of medications under the pretence of restoring biochemical balance, an optimal approach would promote a more discerning use informed by impartial information about their modes of action.

To achieve all the above may sound like a big ask, and it is. The scale of the necessary revisions to the way our society addresses the mental health of its citizens is of such a magnitude as to constitute a revolution. Vested interests will not willingly relinquish their positions of power and privilege. The resistance to radical change will be vigorous, and the battles bloody. But the next 5 to 10 years provide an exceptional opportunity to transform the way we make sense of, and respond to, human misery and suffering. The array of dissenting voices to traditional psychiatry has never been more wide-ranging and compelling. The potential savings to the tax-payer (both short- and long-term) associated with both considerably less requirement for medical expertise, and more judicious use of medication, might provide the essential political motivation for the transformation. Mental health professionals and lay people can each play their parts, by canvassing for change within the current psychiatric system as well as in the broader political arena. The prize of a more compassionate and effective response to human suffering could not be more worthy.

references

American Psychiatric Association (APA). (2014). *Depression.* Retrieved 28 January 2014 from http://www.psychiatry.org/mental-health/depression

Boyle, M. (2013). The persistence of medicalisation: Is the presentation of alternatives part of the problem? In S. Coles, S. Keenan & B. Diamond (Eds.), *Madness Contested: Power and practice* (pp. 3–22). Ross-on-Wye: PCCS Books.

Bracken, P., Thomas, P., Timimi, S., Asen, E., Behr, G., Beuster, C. et al. (2012). Psychiatry beyond the current paradigm. *British Journal of Psychiatry, 201,* 430–4.

Clements, J. & Davies, E. (2013). Prevention of psychosis: Creating societies where more people flourish. In J. Read & J. Dillon (Eds.), *Models of*

Madness: Psychological, social and biological approaches to psychosis (2nd ed.; pp. 295–304). London: Routledge.

Coles, S. (2013). Meaning, madness and marginalisation. In S. Coles, S. Keenan & B. Diamond (Eds.), *Madness Contested: Power and practice* (pp. 42–55). Ross-on-Wye: PCCS Books.

Crawford, M.J., Aldridge, T., Bhui, K., Rutter, D., Manley, C., Weaver, T. et al. (2003). User involvement in the planning and delivery of mental health services: A cross-sectional survey of service users and providers. *Acta Psychiatrica Scandinavica, 107*(6), 410–14.

Davies, H.T.O. (2002). Understanding organisational culture in reforming the National Health Service. *Journal of the Royal Society of Medicine, 95*, 140–2. Retrieved 28 January 2014 from http://www.ncbi.nlm.nih.gov/pmc/articles/PMC1279486/

DCP. (2013). *Division of Clinical Psychology Position Statement on the Classification of Behaviour and Experience in Relation to Functional Psychiatric Diagnoses: Time for a paradigm shift.* Retrieved 31 March 2014 from http://dxrevisionwatch.files.wordpress.com/2013/05/position-statement-on-diagnosis-master-doc.pdf

Dillon, J., Bullimore, P., Lampshire, D. & Chamberlin, J. (2013). The work of experience-based experts. In J. Read & J. Dillon (Eds.), *Models of Madness: Psychological, social and biological approaches to psychosis* (2nd ed.; pp. 305–18). London: Routledge.

Donelan-McCall, N., Eckenrode, J. & Olds, D. (2009). Home visiting for the prevention of child maltreatment. *Pediatric Clinics of North America, 56*, 389–403.

Government Office for Science. (2008). *Foresight Project: Mental Capital and Wellbeing. Final Project Report – Executive Summary.* Retrieved 28 January 2014 from https://www.gov.uk/government/uploads/system/uploads/attachment_data/file/292453/mental-capital-wellbeing-summary.pdf

Johnstone, L. (2000). *Users and Abusers of Psychiatry: A critical look at psychiatric practice* (2nd ed.). London: Routledge.

Johnstone, L., Dillon, J. & Fernando, S. (2013). *Western Psychiatry in Crisis: UK psychiatry re-positions itself.* Retrieved 2 April 2014 from http://www.madinamerica.com/2013/07/western-psychiatry-in-crisis-uk-psychiatry-re-positions-itself/

Lieberman, J. (2013). *DSM-5*: Caught between mental illness stigma and anti-psychiatry prejudice. *Scientific American.* Retrieved 24 March 2014 from http://blogs.scientificamerican.com/mind-guest-blog/2013/05/20/dsm-5-caught-between-mental-illness-stigma-and-anti-psychiatry-prejudice/

Longden, E., Corstens, D. & Dillon, J. (2013). Recovery, discovery and revolution: The work of Intervoice and the Hearing Voices Movement. In

S. Coles, S. Keenan & B. Diamond (Eds.), *Madness Contested: Power and practice* (pp. 161–80). Ross-on-Wye: PCCS Books.

MacMillan, H., Wathen, C., Barlow, J., Fergusson, D., Leventhal, J. & Taussig, H. (2009). Interventions to prevent child maltreatment and associated impairment. *The Lancet, 373,* 250–66.

Mental Health Europe. (2013). *More Harm than Good: DSM 5 and exclusively biological psychiatry must be completely rethought.* Retrieved 25 March 2014 from http://dxrevisionwatch.files.wordpress.com/2013/05/more-harm-than-good-dsm-5-and-exclusively-biological-psychiatry-must-be-completely-rethought-1.pdf

Mikton, C. & Butchart, A. (2009). Child maltreatment prevention. *Bulletin of the World Health Organization, 87,* 353–61.

Moncrieff, J. (2008). *The Myth of the Chemical Cure: A critique of psychiatric drug treatment.* Basingstoke: Palgrave Macmillan.

Moncrieff, J. (2013). *The Bitterest Pills: The troubling story of antipsychotic drugs.* Basingstoke: Palgrave Macmillan.

Mosher, L. (1999). Soteria and other alternatives to acute psychiatric hospitalization: A personal and professional review. *Journal of Nervous and Mental Disease, 187,* 142–9. Retrieved 25 March 2014 from http://www.moshersoteria.com/articles/soteria-and-other-alternatives-to-acute-psychiatric-hospitalization/

Priebe, S., Burns, T. & Craig, T. (2013). The future of academic psychiatry may be social. *British Journal of Psychiatry, 202,* 319–20.

Raine, A., Mellingen, K., Liu, J., Venables, P. & Mednick, S. (2003). Effects of environmental enrichment at ages 3–5 years on schizotypal personality and antisocial behavior at ages 17 and 23 years. *American Journal of Psychiatry, 160,* 1627–35.

Repper, J. & Perkins, R. (2012). Recovery: A journey of discovery for individuals and services. In P. Phillips, T. Sandford & C. Johnston, (Eds.), *Working in Mental Health: Practice and policy in a changing environment* (pp. 71–80). Oxford: Routledge.

Sainsbury Centre for Mental Health. (2009). *Implementing Recovery: A new framework for organisational change.* Position paper. London: Sainsbury Centre for Mental Health.

Sartorius, N. (2002). Iatrogenic stigma of mental illness: Begins with behaviour and attitudes of medical professionals, especially psychiatrists. *British Medical Journal, 324,* 1470–1.

Szmukler, G. (2010). *How Mental Health Law Discriminates Unfairly Against People with Mental Illness.* Retrieved 17 April 2014 from http://www.gresham.ac.uk/lectures-and-events/how-mental-health-law-discriminates-unfairly-against-people-with-mental-illness

Tait, L. & Lester, H. (2005). Encouraging user involvement in mental health services. *Advances in Psychiatric Treatment, 11,* 168–75.

United Nations. (2006). *United Nations Convention on the Rights of Persons with Disabilities.* Retrieved 15 April 2014 from http://www.un.org/disabilities/convention/conventionfull.shtml

Winerman, L. (2013). NIMH funding to shift away from DSM categories. *American Psychological Association,* July/August 2013. Retrieved 25 March 2013 from http://www.apa.org/monitor/2013/07-08/nimh.aspx

World Health Organization (WHO). (2014). *Mental Health: A state of well-being.* Retrieved 21 September 2014 from http://www.who.int/features/factfiles/mental_health/en/

index

The *Straight Talking Introduction to …* series

Psychiatric Drugs *Joanna Moncrieff*
The Causes of Mental Health Problems *John Read & Pete Sanders*
Children's Mental Health Problems *Sami Timimi*
Being a Mental Health Service User *Peter Beresford*
Psychological Treatments for Mental Health Problems *David Pilgrim*
Caring for Someone with Mental Health Problems *Jen Kilyon & Theresa Smith*
Psychiatric Diagnosis *Lucy Johnstone*

A pocket-sized, good-value series of succinct, thought-provoking introductions ideal for students in all mental health disciplines, psychiatric service users, carers and indeed everyone with an interest in mental health. The authors are acknowledged leaders in their respective specialist fields with reputations for clear thinking, realistic, compassionate approaches and straight talking.

Psychiatry in Context:
Experience, meaning and communities
Philip Thomas

ISBN 978 1 906254 72 8

After careful examination of the problems of psychiatric diagnosis, treatments, scientific models of madness, and neuroscience, Thomas goes on to demonstrate how contextual factors are central to mental distress. He proposes that the opportunities we have through narrative, to talk about our experiences and the contexts in which they are embedded, play a vital role in the task of making sense of our lives, in health, when distressed, or when overwhelmed by psychosis.

---

www.pccs-books.co.uk